CRACKING NEUROSCIENCE

An Hachette UK Company
www.hachette.co.uk

First published in Great Britain In 2018 by Cassell,
a division of Octopus Publishing Group Ltd
Carmelite House
50 Victoria Embankment
London EC4Y 0DZ
www.octopusbooks.co.uk

Edited and designed by Whitefox

ISBN 978 1 84403 952 4

A CIP catalogue record for this book is available
from the British Library.

Printed and bound in China

10 9 8 7 6 5 4 3 2 1

Publishing Director Trevor Davies
Production Controller Katie Jarvis

CRACKING
NEUROSCIENCE

JON TURNEY

CONTENTS

INTRODUCTION

Science, I reckon, is our best way of figuring out the world.
Neuroscience strives to understand the thing that does the
figuring out: the brain. It is an enterprise full of astonishment.
The brain itself is astonishing. It is an organ of the body, earning
its keep by helping us survive. It is made of the same stuff as
heart, lungs, liver, or kidneys – blood and tissue, themselves
harbouring minute, intricately organized cells. But it's an
assembly of cells like no other. Somehow, they interact to
achieve remarkable feats. Our brain doesn't pump blood, suck
air, neutralize toxins or filter out waste. But look what it does do:
perception; decision; action; awareness; feeling; thinking.

These are things other blobs of tissue can't even dream of. Dreams are confined to brains, too. Our own brain is the only living entity that can wonder about itself. In fact, it is the only thing we know (so far) that can do that in the universe.

For a long stretch, that wondering led mostly to speculation. Recently, though, there is new cause for astonishment: the extent to which the human brain has yielded to its own curiosity. Ingenious new ways of looking inside have allowed the advent of a neuroscience worthy of the name. Science can develop through startling insights, big ideas, conceptual breakthroughs. Often, though, it's driven by advances in instrumentation that reveal things never seen before. That's true of neuroscience now.

A slew of new techniques has generated an ocean of data, from human brains and those of other species you will meet in this book, including worms, sea-slugs, squid, fruit flies, bees, and even lobsters.

Researchers are trawling this ocean for new insights into how the brain is built, and how it works. We know more about the first, but even there the answers often throw up intriguing new questions.

Meantime, the brain remains a thing of mystery and wonder. There's no guarantee that this evolved complex of cells, chemicals and electricity can understand itself completely. Thinking about the brain is still thinking about the thing that is thinking, which is hard. But we certainly have more to think *about* today than ever before. Start here.

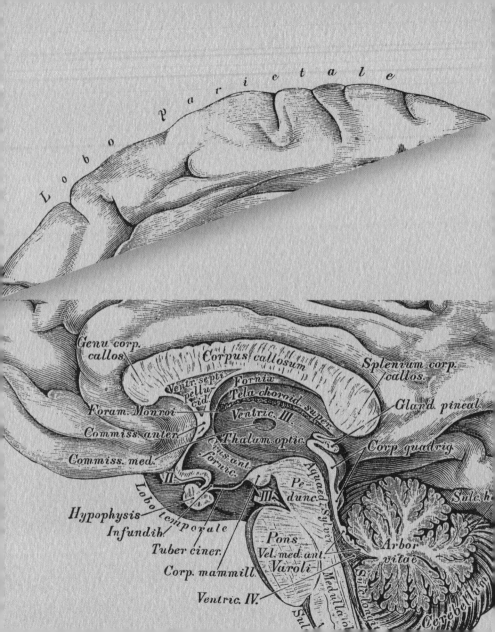

- CHAPTER 1 -

UNPACKING
THE BRAIN

Lobo occipitale

INSIDE THE HEAD

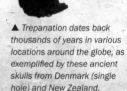

When the ape-men in Stanley Kubrick's film *2001: A Space Odyssey* take up bone cudgels, they go for the head in their first fight. That seems a likely early brain-related discovery. Bash someone's skull in, and they don't get up again. Ancient human remains suggest the manoeuvre was regrettably common.

Some remains show a more careful approach to opening the skull. Drilling holes in the brain cases of the living goes back at least 7,000 years. We don't have much idea why it was done, but it suggests an early recognition that important things went on in there.

▲ *Trepanation dates back thousands of years in various locations around the globe, as exemplified by these ancient skulls from Denmark (single hole) and New Zealand.*

▼ *A scene from Stanley Kubrick's 2001: A Space Odyssey.*

By the time of classical Greece, brain and heart vied for the status of most vital organ. Hippocrates, Western medicine's founding hero, argued around 400 BCE. that the brain was the seat of sensation. He probably saw dissections that revealed sensory nerves entering the brain. He also believed the odd, pulpy mass inside the skull was central to thought. That ran counter to a long-standing idea that the more obviously active heart was, well, at the heart of things. Hippocrates' near-contemporary Aristotle stuck with the older view. The brain, he asserted, was passive, a device for cooling the blood.

Galen, Hippocrates' Roman successor, studied animal brains, and began to theorize about parts of the brain that can be seen with the unaided eye. The big picture was still pretty crude. The outer part of the brain encloses fluid-filled spaces, or ventricles. Could sensations arise when fluid enters the ventricles from the nerves, he wondered? The idea of a hydraulic brain endured beyond the more detailed dissection published by the great anatomist of the European Renaissance, Vesalius, who teased apart the heads of executed criminals in the cause of science. But Galen paved the way for others to pay more attention to the actual brain stuff, rather than what we now call cerebrospinal fluid.

◀ *Hippocrates.*
▶ *Aelius Galenus (Galen).*

THOMAS WILLIS ANATOMIZES THE BRAIN

"The cerebrum is the primary seat of the rational soul in man, and of the sensitive soul in animals. It is the source of movements and ideas."

If you're thinking those words sound like a blend of ancient and modern, you have it right. The English anatomist Thomas Willis is a founder of brain science. His 1664 masterpiece *Cerebri Anatome*, or maybe its translator from the Latin, gave us the word neurology. Yet Willis's neurology still worked with several types of soul or spirits, which his predecessors had located in the ventricles of the brain. He compared species' anatomy to discover how differences in brain structures could account for the immortal soul possessed by man, but not by animals.

Willis qualified as a doctor in monarchist Oxford, an intellectual hothouse during and after the English Civil War. After the war, he developed an almost manic interest in dissection – his investigations taking in silkworms, oysters, lobsters, and earthworms. But the comparison was always with people. We can imagine him, in his Oxford rooms, perhaps directing the rapid dissection of fresh corpses by his student Richard Lower,

◀ *Thomas Willis.*

noting details that were later drawn by Christopher Wren. They probably tried to preserve the brain tissue in alcohol and vinegar – not very effective – so speed was vital.

Somehow, he produced descriptions and drawings that went beyond previous anatomists, tracing new nerves and blood vessels, and naming many distinct parts of the soft tissue. It was a crucial stage in the gradual shift of focus from ventricular fluids to other key structures of the brain.

Allied with this was a new approach to theorizing. Willis related psychiatric conditions to differences he saw in the brains of deceased patients. His idea that headaches begin when extra blood flow to the brain makes swollen vessels compress cranial nerves was widely believed until the end of the 20th century.

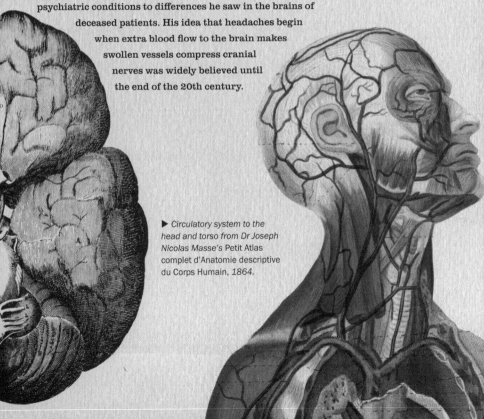

▶ *Circulatory system to the head and torso from Dr Joseph Nicolas Masse's* Petit Atlas complet d'Anatomie descriptive du Corps Humain, *1864.*

LOSING (PART OF) YOUR MIND

Careful dissection established a clearer picture of brain anatomy. The blob of soft tissue at the top of the spinal cord has a complex structure, the two wrinkly hemispheres each subdivided into many other identifiable regions. These were painstakingly labelled, usually in Latin. That's a pity for present-day students of the brain. Early anatomists saw a vermis (a worm), a hippocampus (a sea horse), a colliculus (little hill), even a thalamus (a bed chamber).

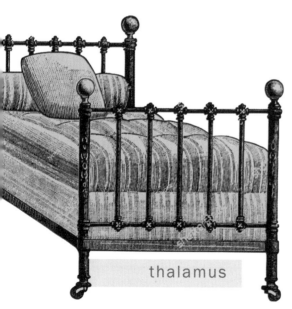

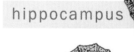

hippocampus

thalamus

The question arose: do different bits do different things? Removing a piece of brain offers clues, and sometimes this happens through accident or disease. Matching missing parts to some loss of function isn't conclusive. Taking out a car's starter motor immobilizes it, but it isn't what drives the vehicle. But mapping deficits began to show which brain regions are involved in which activities – cerebral localization in the trade.

In 1861 Paul Broca presented a case study of a French patient nicknamed "Tan". Aside from that single word, Tan had lost the power of speech 21 years before he died, though he could still curse when something made him angry. Postmortem, Broca found a lesion in the left-hand front of the cerebral cortex. Other similar cases, induced by stroke or even sword wounds, led him to suggest that speech loss, or aphasia, resulted when what is still known as Broca's area is damaged.

Not long after, in the 1870s, Carl Wernicke in Germany defined a separate type of aphasia, in which people can still speak but cannot understand what they hear. This he located to a different region, now known as Wernicke's area.

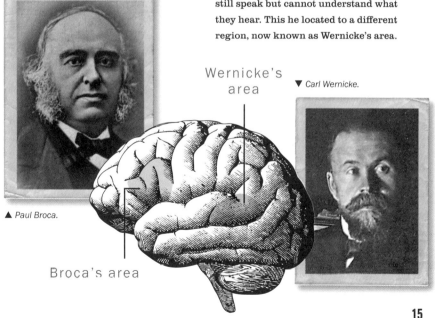

Wernicke's area

▼ Carl Wernicke.

▲ Paul Broca.

Broca's area

Broca and Wernicke's findings revived efforts to localize functions in the brain. They undermined arguments made 50 years earlier by Pierre Flourens, who maintained that although some functions are dependent on the cortex, for example, they are evenly distributed throughout that outer layer of the brain.

Flourens' own target was an elaborate cerebral localization map devised – with no attention to the interior of the brain – by the phrenologist Franz Joseph Gall (see Box). He challenged Gall by removing sections of animal brains, and monitoring the effects. He found almost no specific links between brain regions and functions. Critics charged that he removed brain tissue in slices, probably damaging many specialized regions at once, but his experiments were widely seen as demolishing phrenology, and localization along with it. It was an early skirmish in a frequently renewed controversy – do brain capacities depend on special subregions, or on the whole organ?

Flourens' careful experimentation also prefigured a headline finding from recent neuroscience. Although he knew that brain lesions do not heal, some of his animals recovered from their operations. This we can now see as early evidence of the impressive plasticity of the organ. Damage one part and, in time, another portion may adapt to do the same job – a fact hugely important to stroke patients, among others.

◄ Jean Pierre Flourens.

PHRENOLOGY

Franz Joseph Gall was the greatest brain anatomist since Willis. But the German is remembered not for fine dissection but for his idea that you might read someone's character without delving inside the skull. In the late 18th century, he developed a beautiful scheme resting on two ideas. Specific psychological traits are tied to specific areas of the brain. And differences in the size of those areas can be seen from outside the head.

With much brandishing of dividers to measure skull bones, and character assessments in Gall's own brash style, he produced maps of 27 characters or "faculties", ranging from mirthfulness to benevolence, acquisitiveness, and philoprogenitiveness, or parental love. Eight were specific to humans, including regions conferring abilities for music, poetry, arithmetic, mechanics and religion.

The diagrammed models of skulls with each area neatly outlined now look quaint but were taken seriously well into the 19th century in spite of evidence that the brain does not affect the bumps and hollows of the skull.

▲
Illustrations from Vaught's Practical Character Reader, *by L A Vaught, 1902, indicate how the shape of the head and facial features define a person's character.*

▶ *Franz Joseph Gall, German Phrenologist.*

SHATTERED WORLDS

**Making a contribution to knowledge is
scant consolation for losing part of your
brain. Still, injuries and war wounds
have allowed some unlucky folk to move
neuroscience forward.**

Most celebrated is Phineas Gage, a US
railway worker who survived when the
hefty rod he used for tamping explosives
blew through the front of his skull. His

▲ *Phineas Gage.*

▼ *This lithograph, published in 1850, shows the head injury to Phineas Gage that led to
important advances in understanding how the human brain works.*

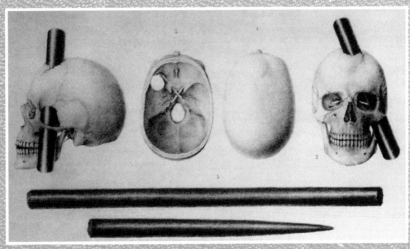

personality changed abruptly after the accident in 1848, the once orderly employee becoming impulsive and foul-mouthed. Gage's transformation in this crude natural "experiment" was taken as evidence that the brain matter removed from his frontal cortex was involved in moral conduct. More recently, historians have reconsidered his later life, when he had regular jobs again. This apparent recovery fits modern ideas about plasticity, too.

Twentieth-century wars ensured more research subjects. After World War II, Alexander Luria in Moscow studied many patients carrying brain injuries. One, the Red Army officer Lev Zasetsky, showed the possibilities, and the limits, of plasticity. Part of his head on one side was shot away, leaving him comatose. When he recovered consciousness, he was free of Gage-type personality changes but could no longer see the right side of objects, including his own body, and had lost the ability to read or write.

Luria treated the man for 25 years. As chronicled in the classic, *The Man with a Shattered World*, Zasetsky gradually relearned some skills, and even managed to compose a 3,000-page journal. Luria's book combines journal extracts with his own commentary, and describes a never-ending struggle to make sense of the world. Zasetsky lived until 1993, 50 years after he was shot, but never recovered full use of language or vision. He left a poignant account of the unanswerable questions such an injury leaves: "Why doesn't my memory function? Why have I not regained my sight, why is there a constant noise in my aching head, why can't I understand human speech properly? It is an appalling task to start again at the beginning and relearn the world which I lost when I was wounded, to piece it together again from tiny separate fragments into a single whole."

▲ *Alexander Luria.*

SEEING NEURONS

Thomas Willis might have looked at brains through a microscope after dissection. Robert Hooke worked for a time as his assistant, and Hooke's pioneering microscopy was the talk of the scientific world a few years later. But Willis wouldn't have seen much. There are just too many neurons and other cells and blood vessels in the brain, and they are too tangled up, for microscopic detail to show.

A clearer view didn't come for another 200 years, after the idea that living creatures are made of cells had taken hold. Camillo Golgi in Italy discovered a new method for staining cells in 1873. Unlike earlier treatments, it showed the whole of a neuron – with all its delicate tendril-like connections. Crucially, the stain only affected a few per cent of the cells in a thin slice of brain. The basic structure of neurons was revealed, uncluttered.

The Spaniard Santiago Ramón y Cajal took up Golgi's method a decade

◀ Camillo Golgi and his stain.

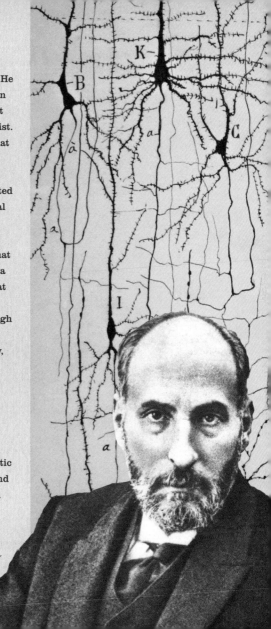

later and devoted the rest of his life to analysing how neurons are arranged. He claimed to have observed over a million neurons, a tiny fraction of the total but vastly more than any other microscopist.

Golgi, perhaps overwhelmed by what he had seen, maintained that the cell theory didn't really apply to the brain. All the structures he saw were connected in one giant network, he believed. Cajal maintained that neurons were still cells. He could see the innumerable connections between them, but held that each cell was bounded. There must be a gap, be it ever so small, between cells at the apparent point of contact.

He couldn't actually see it yet, though – the controversy wasn't definitively settled until well into the next century, when electron microscopes boosted magnification. Golgi and Cajal shared the Nobel Prize in Physiology or Medicine in 1906 despite upholding contrary doctrines about neurons. Today, Cajal is remembered for more than seeing neurons as cells. His artistic skills rivalled his scientific acumen, and his many beautiful drawings of neural structures in the cerebral cortex still repay close study.

▶ Santiago Ramón y Cajal and his drawings for the microscopic structure of the brain.

BRAIN WAVES

Mary Shelley had Dr Frankenstein waken his monster by applying "the spark of life" 200 years ago, reminding us that electricity was seen as biologically powerful soon after it came under scientific study. Demonstrations of twitching muscles led to the suggestion that nerves are wires that transmit electrical signals, and that such signals pass toward as well as from the brain.

In the 1870s, German physiologists had the idea of applying electricity to the brain directly. They soon found that applying a small electrode to the exposed brain of a dog could induce movements. More systematic investigation, especially by the Scot David Ferrier, added to the evidence for cerebral localization. As well as the motor strip around the top of the cortex, he found areas linked to sight and hearing. This was another blow to die-hard phrenologists, as none of the areas identified matched their crude head maps.

More delicate electrical probing of the brain is still a useful research tool. Its complement is reading signals from the internal electrical activity of the neural circuitry, now familiar as the electroencephalogram (EEG).

▲ James Whale's 1932 film of Frankenstein showed electricity at work in the lab.

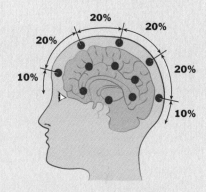

◀ Hans Berger.

20%
20%
20%
20%
20%
10%
10%

▲ Modern EEG uses an array of small electrodes for detailed recording.

HANS BERGER AND THE FIRST ELECTROENCEPHALOGRAM

Sometimes, perseverance pays. Hans Berger became preoccupied with measuring "psychic energy" when he narrowly escaped being crushed by artillery in a military training accident in 1892, when he was 19. An unexpected telegram asking about his welfare later that day, sent at his sister's urging, convinced him telepathy existed.

Seeking its energy source, he tried measuring cerebral blood flow, and began attempts to register electrical activity in human brains in his laboratory in Jena in 1902. His equipment was too crude to record anything but he persisted, on and off, for more than 20 years. In 1924, he tried a new rig with two large electrodes – tinfoil sheets – on the forehead and the back of the head, a vacuum tube amplifier and a galvanometer, and finally saw an electrical trace from an intact skull, from his son Klaus.

Working solo, he spent five years refining his results before publishing the first paper on his "Elektrenkephalogramm" in 1929. It featured in the German press as a "brain mirror", but there was little reaction from other scientists until his findings were confirmed in 1934 in the UK.

SEEING INSIDE

Extracting electrical signals via EEG pointed the way to a new approach to neuroscientific observation – getting information out without intruding directly on the brain. Techniques for doing that reliably account for much of the explosive growth of modern brain science.

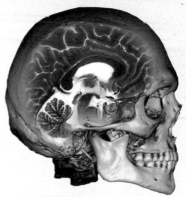

▲ The skull, pictured by combining CT and MRI scans.

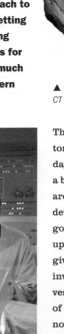

▲ Medicine, and brain scanning, would be so much easier if we really had Star Trek technology.

The first was the computerized tomography (CT) scan, familiar these days from widespread medical use. It is a beefed-up X-ray, in which thin sections are assembled by computer to create a detailed structural image. It's not much good for soft tissue, so doesn't often crop up in neuroscience research, but can give good images of tumours. It's also invaluable for getting pictures of blood vessels, though that calls for injection of a chemical to improve contrast – noninvasive is a relative term.

Researchers are more likely to want access to a magnetic resonance imaging (MRI) machine. That's the thing that looks like something out of *Star Trek* that you roll inside headfirst, as long as you don't have anything inside you that will react badly to a strong magnetic field, like a heart pacemaker or a metal hip joint. It can generate amazingly detailed pictures of soft tissues, including brains.

MRI is complemented by other techniques in the modern neuroscientific arsenal. EEG is more sophisticated these days, and the newer magnetoencephalography (MEG) may also be used to register electrical activity under the skull. There is also information to be gleaned from stimulating brains with magnets (transcranial magnetic stimulation) and monitoring the results.

More refined, and even more high-tech approaches can yield data about chemical activity in the brain. As with X-rays, they involve chemical injection, but are otherwise noninvasive. The science fictional sounding positron emission tomography tracks the paths of injected radioactive tracers that have an affinity for a chemical of interest, usually a neurotransmitter.

The catalogue goes on, but all these methods allow neuroscientists to amass information about brain states and structures that would have been inaccessible only a few decades ago.

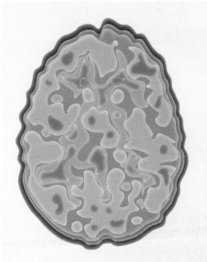

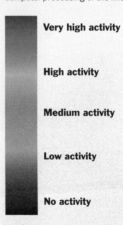

Scans are colour-coded during computer-processing of the image.

Very high activity

High activity

Medium activity

Low activity

No activity

SEEING BLOOD

Looking inside live brains is now routine, thanks especially to MRI. It seems almost magical, but the results are so beguiling it's important to understand its strengths and weaknesses.

The nuclear magnetic part refers to the magnetic properties of atomic nuclei, especially hydrogen nuclei (protons). The physics need not bother us, except that it permits detection of which chemical elements are where in a sample. In regular MRI this yields very detailed structural information.

Neuroscience's other favourite is "functional" MRI (fMRI). That relies on a read-out of blood flow and how much oxygen it carries. Oxygen supplies energy, so an increase probably means something nearby needs some. Neurons need energy to fire and to release neurotransmitters, so an active brain region uses more oxygen. fMRI shows where this is happening.

We know the brain regulates blood supply closely, and rapidly – it may even anticipate which regions are about to become active. But the signal coming from the scanner here is indirect. Actual brain cell activity is mainly electrical.

And while MRI has pretty good spatial resolution, the smallest region detectable still has hundreds of thousands of neurons. And it takes several seconds to capture the data that shows increases in blood flow, while neurons work much faster. All this means that inferences like "this brain region gets more blood when the person in the scanner is doing/thinking about **X**, so must be essential for **X** to happen" are too simple.

Such results need to be considered from lots of angles. How many brains were studied? Are there comparisons with subjects with alterations in the parts of the brain in question? And how do the results compare with what other ways into brains – like direct electrical recording – tell us?

▶ *Resin cast of the blood supply to the brain.*

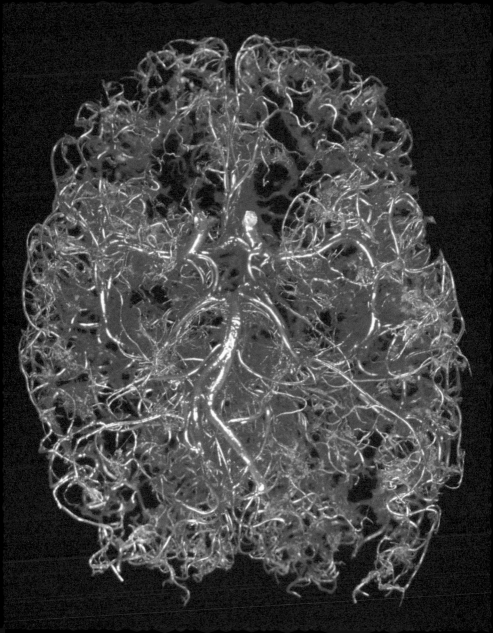

GETTING THE MESSAGE

Getting brain read-outs from outside is invaluable. However, if you want real details of the signals within the brain there's no substitute for direct contact. Long after everyone knew that neurons generate electrical impulses, researchers remained frustrated because they couldn't find tools fine enough to tap into a single neuron, the basic unit of operation in the nervous system.

The breakthrough was not technical, but zoological. In the 1930s, British physiologist J Z Young drew attention to a special nerve in the squid. These sea creatures need a fast signal to activate their jet propulsion system but have never evolved the insulated nerve fibres that allow speedy electrical transmission. They get round this by growing giant nerve fibres (axons) from the relevant neurons. These are as much as 1mm (³⁄₆₄in) across, big enough to allow researchers to push a tiny electrode inside the fibre. It also makes it easy to wash out the axon's internal fluid and replace it with one of known chemistry.

Two other Brits, Alan Hodgkin and Andrew Huxley set up an electrode, amplifier and recorder to investigate exactly what happened inside the squid axon, millisecond by millisecond. Between 1939 and 1952, with a lengthy interruption for war work, they worked out how nerve impulses are carried by abrupt movements of charged ions passing across nerve membranes, the basis of our modern, molecular understanding of how neural circuits carry signals (see Chapter 4 for details). They published the results in a sequence of five historic papers in 1952.

◀ *Andrew Huxley.*

Nowadays, recording the firing of single neurons is possible in less obliging species. In fact, researchers can record signals on smaller scales still, using techniques that involve gently sucking a tiny portion of a neural membrane part way into the tip of a glass electrode a micrometre or so across. German neuroscientists Bert Sakmann and Erwin Neher showed in the 1970s that this method could isolate the individual channels in the cell membrane that charged ions pass through, and worked out how they are controlled. Like the British pair, they shared the Nobel Prize in Physiology or Medicine.

◀ *Alan Hodgkin with radioastronomer and fellow Nobellist, Martin Ryle.*

LABELLING WITH LIGHT

There are layers within layers in the brain's structure. New imaging and
labelling techniques are still helping researchers get a fix on cells, networks
of cell connections, and larger-scale interactions inside the brain.

One technique unites fancy molecular
biology with sophisticated physics to
produce the best pictures of neurons yet.
Two-photon microscopy uses brilliant
infrared lasers to illuminate a sample.
If their light falls on the right molecules

they absorb two photons – hence the
name – and emit a single photon of
visible light. The physics of the set-up
means the technique works well for
scanning living tissue rapidly. The
fluorescent target must be introduced

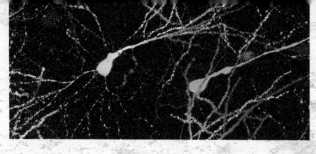

◀ Mouse neurons labelled with green fluorescent protein.

into the tissue artificially. The first time it was done for a single live neuron, by injection, the chemical quickly spread through all the cell's branches and twigs. It lit up "like a Christmas tree", according to the researcher, Karel Svoboda.

The real payoff comes from combining this technique with genetic manipulation. Some jellyfish and corals make proteins that fluoresce with a slightly eerie green light – and the protein genes can be slipped into neurons of developing mice via an engineered virus. When the foreign DNA works properly, in about one neuron in 10,000, the cell makes its own fluorescent molecules. As with the Golgi stain (page 20), the selectivity helps by producing uncluttered images when laser light of the right frequency shines.

Better still, the technique does no damage. You can photograph the same neuron over and over again in the intact brain. This allows researchers to track the tiniest changes in cell structure and connection, a great help in testing theories of memory, for example (see Chapter 7).

Since the fluorescent proteins are added by the researchers, there is no need to stick to naturally occurring ones. That would be boring. Protein engineers are now making fluorescent proteins that combine with other cell components to register changes in calcium levels, for instance. The result is essentially a neuron that is dark but lights up under the microscope when it fires – imaging the essence of brain activity in real time.

◀ Tubastrea hard coral fluorescing at night.

BEHOLD, THE CONNECTOME?

The riches gathered from observing brains with new instruments are encouraging neuroscientists to think big. The grandest plan is for a complete map of all the connections between neurons in a human brain – the so-called connectome. It's insanely ambitious. The number of cells and circuits involved makes the human genome project – which sequenced a mere 3 billion units of DNA – look a doddle by comparison. But the cash invested, and the spur to push the technology, will matter, even if the final goal is distant.

The US-led Human Connectome Project, launched in 2009, is starting with MRI. A variant of MRI known as diffusion imaging can detect the direction of nerve fibres, and map the brain's basic wiring diagram on a relatively large scale – thousands of fibres at a time.

The project has already unveiled a new map of the cerebral cortex based on scans of 210 adults. The resulting mountain of data was analysed using a machine-learning algorithm. The map outlined 180 different cortical areas, more than half of them

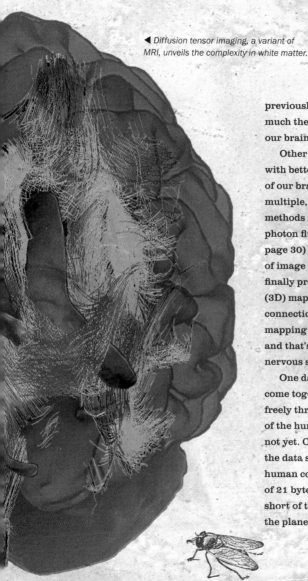

◀ *Diffusion tensor imaging, a variant of MRI, unveils the complexity in white matter.*

previously unknown – a sign of how much there still is to discover about our brains.

Other groups are testing methods with better resolution on tiny portions of our brains or on other species: multiple, coordinated imaging methods in the macaque brain; two-photon fluorescence scanning (see page 30) in mice; painstaking analysis of image slices in the fruit fly. The last finally produces three-dimensional (3D) maps that can show every connection of every neuron – although mapping 60,000 cells took ten years and that's only a quarter of the fly's nervous system.

One day, all these techniques will come together and allow us to navigate freely through a 3D virtual rendering of the human brain at any scale. Just not yet. One informed estimate puts the data storage needed for a full human connectome at 10 to the power of 21 bytes – or a zettabyte: not far short of the total computer storage on the planet today.

PICTURING THE BRAIN

Imaging and mapping of many kinds offers a fantastic set of ways of investigating the brain. They cut through clutter to visualize key features of interest. That can leave us with a weirdly spacious impression of a solid, if jelly-like, organ.

This applies not so much to the pictures built up from MRI, although they have their own limitations (see page 26), but is something to bear in mind when looking at pictures of cells.

▶ The cellular tangle in the cerebral cortex: dendrites are shown in red or orange, axons in blue and green and glial branches in yellow.

Suppose you were shrunk to the size of, say, a medium-sized protein molecule, and could roam around among the brain cells. The main thing you would notice is that the brain is astonishingly crowded. Everything is packed in as tightly as it can be.

But that makes it hard to see how it is made. Most pictures of cells and their connections follow the example of Cajal, who could see individual neurons properly because Golgi's new stain allowed him to ignore most of them.

But some image-makers are now putting the full detail back in. The reconstruction opposite, made by researchers at Harvard University, shows *all* the dendrites, axons and branches of glial cells in a 100 micrometre cube of mouse cerebral cortex. That's a volume comparable to a single neuronal cell body.

The landscape is as complex at still smaller scales. One remarkable example is a reconstruction of what a synapse might actually look like, based on counting all of the proteins in and around the point where one neuron

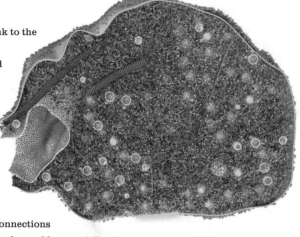

▲ The molecular tangle in a synapse: a single synaptic bouton depicted with its full complement of many different proteins.

connects with another, then building a picture that shows every single one.

This region, the synaptic bouton, is often depicted schematically as a blob filled with small packet-like vesicles of neurotransmitter.

Close up, though, it probably looks more like the image above.

Aside from being rather beautiful, these images are a reminder that pictures of the brain are always a trade-off – leaving out enough detail so we can see the important things, but not taking out so much that vital features of the real brain are missing.

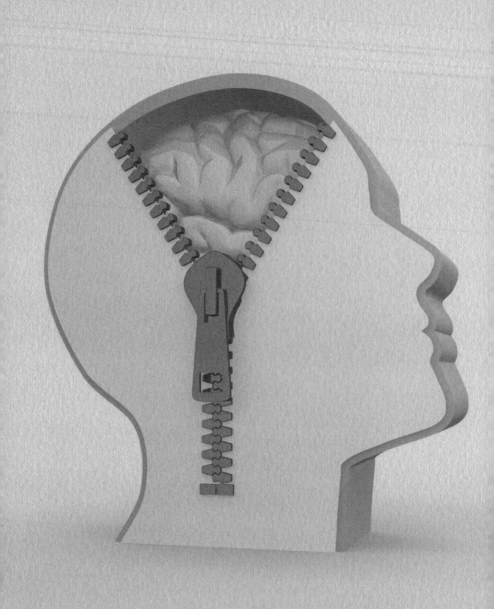

- CHAPTER 2 -

GETTING ACQUAINTED

BRAIN STRUCTURE – FROM ANATOMY TO MOLECULES

You can go into the brain two ways – top down, or bottom up. However you begin, there are many levels of structure to take in, from the way brain regions are wired together to the movement of molecules inside cells. Neuroscience tends to lean toward *reductionism* – taking a thing apart to see how it works – occasionally popping its head up from the bench to consider the wider view. *Holism* – considering the collected bits and pieces as a whole system with its own rules – always has its advocates, too. The two aren't exclusive. You can strive to understand the tiniest parts while acknowledging their part in a larger overarching structure. As with another perennial controversy in the science of us – should we understand how our brains (and minds) operate by investigating cells, circuits and molecules, or studying behaviour? – the best answer is "try a bit of both".

▼ What's on your mind?

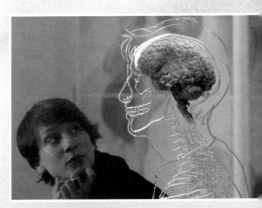

Working that middle ground, where most neuroscientists feel comfortable, calls for knowing the basics about brains, at all levels. This chapter gives an outline of the larger structures – we look closer at cells and molecules in Chapter 4.

Let's start at the top. The nervous system includes the brain and the nerves to and from the rest of the body. A dozen pairs of cranial nerves, mainly serving the head, connect directly to the brain. Another 31 pairs branch out from the spinal cord.

Looking at the brain unmagnified, we can already divide it roughly into three regions, each with fluid-filled spaces (ventricles) and soft cellular tissue.

* **The hindbrain** sits at the top of the spinal cord. Here the brainstem grows first into the medulla, which supports breath and heartbeat, and is attached to the cerebellum, a large mini-organ involved with balance and movement.

* **The midbrain** region is small and contains clumps of nerve cells (called nuclei, not to be confused with cell nuclei) involved with other basic functions like being awake.

* **The forebrain** is the largest region. It includes the familiar wrinkled cerebral cortex – the part that humans have developed more than any other species – and lots of other smaller bits and pieces.

There, we need to go into more detail.

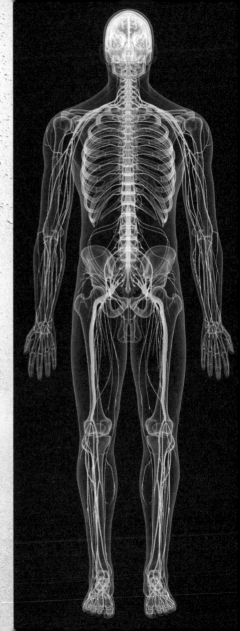

▶ The main pathways of the human nervous system.

NAMING OF PARTS

The forebrain includes a host of different structures and regions. Their names are mostly uninformative, except for historians. But some help basic orientation. The *cerebral cortex*, a thin layer with many folds and grooves, is in two halves – the cerebral hemispheres – connected by a thick nerve bundle, the *corpus callosum*. The latter is part of the *white matter* of the brain, mainly nerve fibres. A common estimate is that there are 161,000km (100,000 miles) of them. White matter contrasts with the *grey matter*, where the cells are. It is grey in dead, dissected brains, but pinkish in a living brain, where blood still flows.

The cortex has been mapped in detail but large-scale divisions into two left–right strips – one the *motor cortex*, one the *sensory cortex* – and four *lobes – frontal, temporal, parietal, occipital –* on each side, are still often referred to.

The cortex surrounds a set of crucial smaller structures. The *thalamus* is a lump of tissue mainly concerned with integrating the work of the other parts of the brain. Just underneath, the pea-sized *hypothalamus* is linked to hormonal

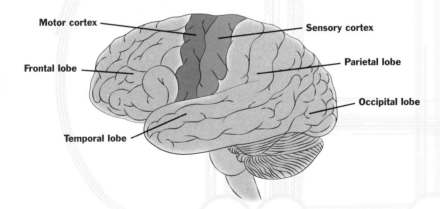

Motor cortex — Sensory cortex

Frontal lobe — Parietal lobe

Occipital lobe

Temporal lobe

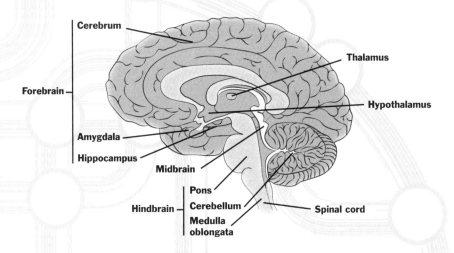

Cerebrum

Forebrain

Thalamus

Hypothalamus

Amygdala

Hippocampus

Midbrain

Pons

Hindbrain — Cerebellum

Medulla
oblongata

Spinal cord

action and to hunger, thirst, and both bodily and sexual heat. The *hippocampus* is a part of the cortex vital for storing, locating and retrieving memories.

Finally, near the hippocampus nestles the *amygdala*, which is involved with emotion, and which helps tinge memories with anger, fear, jealousy or sadness.

All these can be seen in a dissection, though the motor and sensory cortexes just look like the rest of the cerebral cortex and were singled out by prodding brains electrically. But all contain many neurons, and many more connections. Naming them and assigning functions assumes that the brain keeps things in separate

compartments. It does, to some extent – it is modular, in the jargon. But they are all intricately connected, and work with each other, or sometimes against one another, to run the whole show.

They also often make up losses, given time, making it hard to know what serves a particular function. An extreme case here is a woman whose magnetic resonance imaging (MRI) scan revealed she was born with no cerebellum. She had slightly slurred speech and an unusual gait, but was married with a child and only had a medical examination aged 24 for what proved to be an excess of cerebrospinal fluid.

THE SEAT OF REASON?

The human cerebral cortex is big, comparatively speaking, but it's easy to overestimate how big when looking at a whole brain. The cortex is the thin outer layer of grey (pink) matter covering the cerebrum, and is never more than 5mm (¹³⁄₆₄in) deep. It has expanded mainly in one dimension. If the wrinkly cortical layer packed inside our skulls could be flattened out, we would see a sheet of cells the size of a tablecloth, perhaps 2m² (21½ft²). Although thin, it still typically weighs more than a kilogram (2lb). It accounts for around four-fifths of the mass of the brain, but only perhaps one-fifth of the total number of neurons.

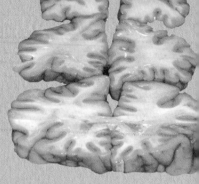

▲ The cerebral cortex partially opened out.

The bulges and dents in the naturally wrinkly cortex have their own names – *gyri* and *sulci* respectively. They don't have any special significance, as far as we know.

On smaller scales, the basic unit in the cortex seems to be a roughly cylindrical structure, about 0.5mm (⅟₆₄in) across. Each typically includes 10,000 neurons and as many as a million synaptic connections. In most of the cortex (the portion known as the neocortex) each cylinder reveals six layered sheets of cells, organized differently in terms of the type, size and density of neurons. Some of the layers are mainly devoted to connections between different

◀ The surface wrinkles of our brain allow us to grow a larger cortex.

molecular layer

external granular layer

layer of small and medium-sized pyramids

internal granular layer

ganglionic layer

polymorphic cell layer

white matter

parts of the cortex – within or between the two halves of the brain – some with linking to other brain regions.

This vast territory has been mapped every which way. The first useful map was based on microscopic surveys of cell types by the German Korbinian Brodmann at the start of the last century. His 40-odd numbered regions are still sometimes used (the cortical layers are numbered, too, using Roman numerals). Nowadays, many more regions have been identified, and we see that the cortex is involved in more or less everything the brain does. As well as "higher" cognitive functions, such as language, the cortex has areas that focus on vision, hearing, motor control, touch, taste and smell. And as Phineas Gage – whose massive frontal lobe injury removed chunks from what are formally known as the orbital and medial prefrontal cortex – taught us, it helps shape personality and behaviour.

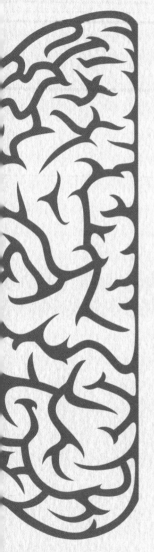

ONE BRAIN: TWO HALVES?

Ours is a brain of two halves. Virtually all the brain's structures are paired. The cortex has a visible gap between two symmetrical hemispheres. Fat bundles of nerves make hundreds of thousands of connections between the two sides.

This bilateral structure matches the overall body plan of many creatures. It is such a fundamental feature of our world that it's tempting to speculate that it is the source of our tendency to think about things in terms of opposed pairs (light/dark, good/bad, either/or… and many more). It has certainly given rise to many curious features of our neuroanatomy.

The brain parcels out basic jobs carefully, with a twist. The motor cortex in the left hemisphere controls movement on the right side of the body, and vice versa. Portions of visual cortex on each side of the brain have a more subtle division of labour. The right

side interprets signals not from the opposite eye but from the left side of the visual field as seen by each eye.

Some other functions generally favour one side of the brain. Ninety per cent of humans are right-handed, and can control fine finger movements better from their left hemisphere. Similarly, Broca's and Wernicke's areas, linked to language use, are most often on the left side of the cortex. They do develop on the right side in some left-handed people though.

This stark division has led to much research on small differences between the two sides of the brain. The findings can be enigmatic. A few researchers have examined people who are desperate to have one of their apparently healthy legs amputated because it does not feel as if it belongs, a condition few of us can identify with. Most (from a small sample) sought removal of their left leg. That went with discernible differences in MRI scans, mainly on the right-hand side of the cortex. But we have little idea what ties together how the limb feels, the desire to be rid of it, and action here.

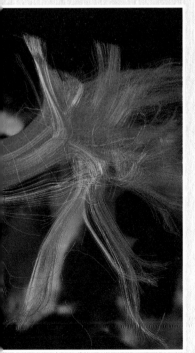

◀ The two hemispheres are richly connected by nerve fibres of the corpus callosum, shown here in red by diffusion tensor imaging.

45

SPLIT BRAINS

People can manage after losing surprisingly large bits of brain. Surgeons sometimes cut the main cable between the two hemispheres – the corpus callosum – in patients with severe epilepsy. It's a last-ditch effort to stop seizures spreading from one side of the brain to the other, but it also provides intriguing subjects for further study.

Patients don't feel any different after the operation, and interact normally in everyday life. But US researcher Roger Sperry showed in the 1960s that in some ways their divided brains operated as separate systems, even though, as he wrote of the first subject, "In casual conversation over a cup of coffee and a cigarette one would hardly suspect that there was anything unusual about him."

Sperry and his student Michael Gazzaniga devised experiments in which each hemisphere received different stimuli. Flash something on one side of the visual field, for example, without time for the eyes to move so it can be seen by the other side of the brain. In this way, they showed that their patient's language was locked up in his left hemisphere. He could not read anything in the left of the visual field (and therefore processed by his right hemisphere), write with the left hand, or respond to spoken commands involving his left arm or leg. But he *could* identify objects blindfolded by feeling them with his left hand.

▲ Roger Sperry.

This was powerful evidence for separation of the hemispheres. And their independence was reinforced when they seemed to work in conflict. The same man could do things with both hands working together, Sperry reported, but "at times the left hand may go off in a distracted way on independent and even antagonistic activities of its own which can be troublesome."

Later patients showed more dramatic conflicts. One child who, unusually, had language abilities on both sides of his brain (there are always exceptions in neuroscience, it seems) gave different answers when questions were directed at one side of his brain or the other. What do you want to be when you grow up? "A racing driver," said one hemisphere. "A draftsman," replied the other. The casual phrase "in two minds" becomes a reality for such subjects.

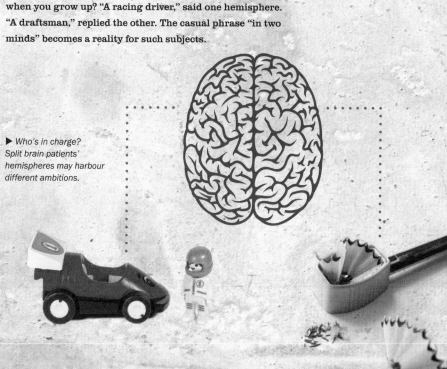

▶ Who's in charge? Split brain patients' hemispheres may harbour different ambitions.

BEYOND LEFT AND RIGHT

That chasm between the two halves of the brain impresses people so much that it has sustained a neuromyth about people being "left brained" or "right brained". It ties in the undoubted division between hemispheres, curious results like Sperry's, some of the cruder aspects of cerebral localization, and the suggestion that everyone has a "dominant" hemisphere.

The basic idea is that some people have better developed logic, maths and language skills (left brainers). Others are less orderly or analytical, but more creative or artistic (right brainers). Such a simple dichotomy should make anyone getting better informed about the brain suspicious. But simplicity appeals, so the idea lives on.

It's wrong for a few reasons. Hardly any abilities are isolated in one hemisphere. Complex cognitive functions may depend on some identifiable portion of the brain, like Broca's area, but invariably involve other regions too. And for those with intact relays between the hemispheres, the two sides of the brain interact continually, with many areas helping to generate our response to any given situation.

Could one hemisphere's inputs and outputs still tend to dominate in all this

▶ The claim that analytical and creative skills lie in different hemispheres is a vast oversimplification.

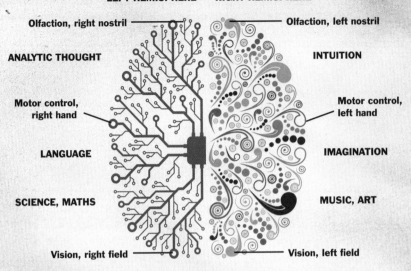

Olfaction, right nostril — Olfaction, left nostril

ANALYTIC THOUGHT   INTUITION

Motor control,
right hand   Motor control,
left hand

LANGUAGE   IMAGINATION

SCIENCE, MATHS   MUSIC, ART

Vision, right field — Vision, left field

▲ *The strong version of left- and right-brain dominance.*
The capitalized labels are the ones to view with suspicion.

dynamic collaboration? It looks very unlikely. A study from the University of Utah in 2013 brought MRI to bear on the problem. The team examined brain scans from 1,011 people, taken from a neuroscientific database, and measured the density of their grey matter at thousands of different locations in each hemisphere.

Their analysis showed that there are networks involved in particular functions – language processing, for instance – that operate in one hemisphere. But they found no evidence that one side of the brain was more influential than the other overall.

In addition, although the idea of a dominant hemisphere is sometimes linked to supposed differences between men and women, they reported no measurable gender difference in their sample.

None of this means that people do not have the differences in personality, or thinking styles, that figure in the "left brained" or "right brained" story. But if so, it is not due to one half of their brain somehow exerting a stronger influence than the other.

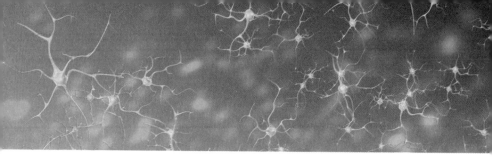

HOW MANY NEURONS CAN YOU SEE?

Science often has numbers you can trust – the speed of light in a vacuum, the charge on an electron, that kind of thing. Neuroscience? Not so much. Take the number of neurons in an adult human brain. For decades, literally every article on the brain told you the average human has 100 billion neurons. No one seems sure where this suspiciously round number came from but, conveniently, it roughly matches a commonly used estimate of the number of stars in the Milky Way, which adds to the "wow" factor.

Imagine counting that many of anything. There must be sampling and multiplication involved. A few years ago, the widely quoted figure came down to 86 billion. That was based on a study which involved completely breaking down the tissue of a few (middle-aged, male) brains,

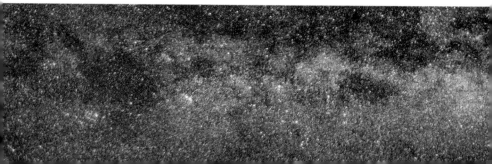

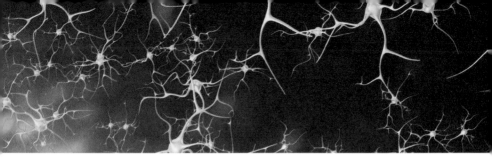

and counting stained cell nuclei in a portion of the resulting soup. That gets round the difficulty of making neurons visible, and the varying density of cells in different parts of the brain. It's probably more accurate, but is still only a best estimate for now.

Similar caution applies to other estimates. The number of other cells – the various types of glial cells, which were the main target of the study just mentioned – is now regarded as roughly equal to the neurons. The number of connections? Well, some neurons really do have 10,000 individual synapses, so you can do the maths.

My favourite brain number is the following heroic calculation, from a widely used textbook. Consider the brain as "a complicated mesh of neural membranes". A typical neuron has a surface area of 250,000μm² (micrometers squared). So 85 billion neurons have a total surface area of 21,250m² (25,414yd²). That's roughly three football (soccer) fields.

Science needs numbers, but bear in mind that numbers in the world of cells are often approximate, at best. The upside? Well, it does mean that you can still make an original contribution to neuroscience if you can count, and do it really carefully.

SMALL, BUT INFLUENTIAL

It is easy to be bedazzled by the cortex, in all its size and complexity. But older, smaller parts of the brain are no less vital. The amygdala and nearby hypothalamus are conspicuous examples. Both are relatively tiny areas that nevertheless contain many subdivisions or nuclei. Both are deeply involved with many other parts of the brain, and help regulate activity both consciously and unconsciously.

AMYGDALA

The amygdala (Greek for almond) is centrally concerned with emotion. It seems to be the first destination for information from the senses – a threatening facial expression, for instance – and triggers rapid emotional responses. These may be modified by further consideration in the cortex, but it lags behind the unconscious, reflexive responses emanating from this corner of the brain. Different parts of the amygdala are linked to aggression, and anxiety. It also appears to be the seat of instinctual fears, like horror of snakes, and ones we can learn, especially if they relate to events that cause physical pain.

HYPOTHALAMUS

The hypothalamus, weighing just a few grams, is also involved in triggering anger and aggression, as well as regulating basic needs and appetites. It connects richly with the autonomic nervous system – the part of the body's network that operates without conscious control – and orchestrates reactions like the "fight or flight" response to perceived danger, with its racing heart, dilated blood vessels, and goose pimples. It also works through influencing the release of hormones, with cascading effects, and responding in turn to hormonal signals.

Amygdala

Hypothalamus

Both these subregions of the brain are still taxing researchers, and are involved in a wide range of other crucial features of life including social behaviour. They are relatively old, evolutionarily speaking, but that does not mean they are only dealing with basic stuff. Amygdala experts like New York University researcher Joseph LeDoux argue that the human brain depends on emotional centres as well as portions that process information in more complex ways to drive decision-making and action.

He is also the leader of perhaps the only neuroscientific rock band, the Amygdaloids.

▼ *Some sounds send shivers down the spine – triggered by the amygdala.*

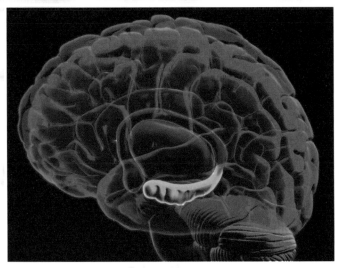

◀ The hippocampus, like many other brain regions, has two symmetrical halves. It lies under the temporal lobes.

THE HIPPOCAMPUS

We don't understand memory too well, but it is pretty certain that developing memories depends on the hippocampus. This small brain region is not where memories are kept (see Chapter 7), but is a kind of clearing house. It helps process experiences that are on the way to becoming memories. Later, it helps coordinate retrieval of stored memories, often from quite different parts of the brain. This can be influenced consciously: when something gives rise to that tantalizing feeling of being "on the tip of your tongue", you are somehow querying your store of memories but not quite getting the response you seek.

▶ *Where to, guv?*
London cab drivers
command the street
map of an unusually
complex city.

The involvement of the hippocampus in laying down new memories has been inferred from extensive studies of brains that lacked this portion – wholly or partly – in both humans and animals. On the other hand, it is also one of the prime sources of evidence of the adaptability of our brains. The modern neuroscientific theme of plasticity extends beyond alterations in detailed wiring to quite large neuroanatomical changes.

The most often cited study here used brain scans to measure the hippocampus in London taxi drivers. They have to deal with a city with hardly any convenient grids of thoroughfares. Getting a licence to drive one of London's black cabs requires would-be drivers to learn 25,000 of the city's tangled streets and how they are joined up, so they can plot 320 routes instantly. "The knowledge" takes some four years to learn. And, as anticipated from animal evidence, researchers found that cabbies had expanded one region of the hippocampus while another shrank. Bus drivers, who have similar stresses and strains from days on the streets but follow a few set routes, did not show these changes. And retired taxi drivers gradually lost them.

This suggests the hippocampus is involved in learning how to navigate spatially, presumably an ancient survival skill that taxi drivers need in a modern form. More recent studies involving people – again in London – moving around with or without sat navs to aid them suggest that different subregions of the same small anatomical item are involved in remembering spatial details and planning routes.

And that's certainly not all it does. Musicians are another group who have yielded interesting evidence of hippocampal changes in MRI studies.

JUST A FEW MORE

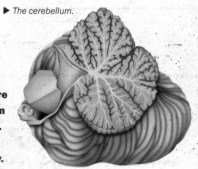

▶ *The cerebellum.*

The basic inventory of identifiable parts of the brain concludes with the thalamus, which is more or less in the middle of our brains, the brainstem beneath it and, just behind that, the cerebellum. Together, they cater for a whole range of basic functions, many of which operate unconsciously.

CEREBELLUM

The word means "little brain" and it does look a bit like an extra cerebrum, right down to its layered structure. It takes care of movement, balance and posture – things you only notice when they go awry. Nevertheless, like the rest of the brain, it has plenty of nerve connections with the cerebral cortex, and there is continual talk between them. And although it only makes up one-tenth of brain mass, it accounts for half the total number of cells and no less than four-fifths of all neurons.

▲ *The brainstem lies at the heart of the brain, just atop the spinal cord.*

▲ *Jean-Dominique Bauby holds his own remarkable testimony, here in the film of his life.*

MEDULLA AND PONS

The remaining named parts, the medulla and pons that make up most of the brainstem, are complex in their own right, and mainly organize bundles of nerves that link the spinal cord to the cerebrum and cerebellum. It is easy to think of them as subordinate to "higher" functions, but they underpin everything else. Some kind of functioning life can be preserved with little or no cerebral cortex. Then there are those rare cases of people born without a cerebellum, some of whom show remarkably little effect from growing up with a large portion of their brain missing. But a severe injury to the brainstem is normally terminal.

LOCKED-IN SYNDROME

In 1995, French journalist Jean-Dominique Bauby had a stroke that left him comatose for some weeks. As he relates in his 1997 memoir *The Diving Bell and the Butterfly*, he regained consciousness three weeks later but had no control over his body muscles. Damage to his brainstem had left him completely paralysed though fully conscious, a case of what was defined in the 1960s as locked-in syndrome.

Like some other locked-in patients, Bauby could still blink (with one eye) and he learned to communicate in this way. Blinking at the right stop in the alphabet allowed him to choose letters, and make words. Remarkably, he completed the book, using around 200,000 eye-blinks over ten months, but died of pneumonia days after publication.

CELLS ARE US: BUT WHICH ONES?

Remove a human brain from the skull and put it on a lab bench and it flattens out slightly – less than a balloon full of water would, more than a lump of putty. It doesn't have much in the way of internal support. As we have seen, it has plenty of large-scale structure but it is also a mass of cells that, protected by layers of skin, bone and membrane, are specialized for work that is mental, not physical.

There are a lot of blood vessels – around a metre of the finest ones in every cubic millimetre of cortex. They do the same as blood vessels elsewhere. But brain tissue is otherwise very distinctive. Like other specialized organs, it has unique types of cells.

They fall into two main types.

* **Neurons** are the ones that have dominated professional and popular discussion of brains for a century.

They were easier to see, after Golgi, and they look more obviously different from other cells – as we'll discuss in detail.

* **Glial cells** were long assumed to be of less interest. Some perform clearly defined supporting roles, such as the cells that furnish nerves with a fatty myelin sheath that speeds up the rate they can transmit signals – oligodendrocytes – and the brain's own immune cells, the microglia.

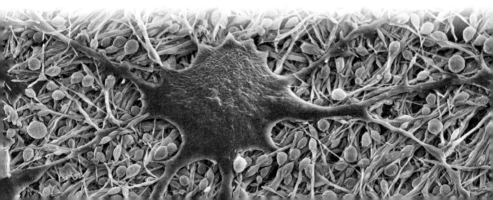

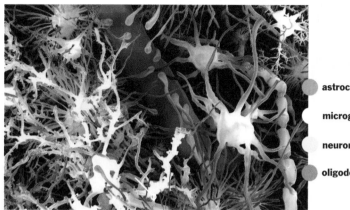

astrocyte

microglia

neuron

oligodendrocyte

▲ *There are many types of cells in the brain.*

A third type of glial cells, astrocytes, which account for half the brain by volume, were seen for a long time as relatively passive spectators. But as often happens in biology, they were designated as less interesting out of imperfect knowledge. Recently, some astrocytes, at least, have been revealed as more neuron-like. Some of them release their own small packets of neurotransmitter chemicals. And they can respond to local neuron action, providing one of several ways that the fine detail of nerve signals can be adjusted, or modulated in scientific language.

There is clearly more to unravel about this relatively self-effacing cell type. The moral probably holds good for other brain features. Just because something fails to look interesting with the observation technique you happen to be using, doesn't mean it isn't doing something important. And cells that are close enough to interact, whether via chemical message or nerve linkages, probably are working together even if you can't quite see how.

◀ *A single glial cell seen under an electron microscope.*

MEET A NEURON

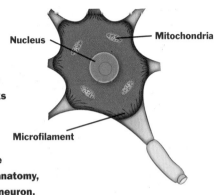

Nucleus

Mitochondria

Microfilament

Neurons are the cells still often, and fairly accurately, described as the building blocks of the brain. They vary a good deal in fine structure, and in activity – both chemical and electrical. They need a chapter to themselves (Chapter 4). But since we have covered the most basic features of brain anatomy, here is the simple anatomy of an average neuron.

Dendrites

Nucleus

Cell body

Myelin Sheath

Direction of nerve impulse

Axon

Axon terminals

Synapse

It has a blobby bit in the middle, the cell body. This is the part where you can check the features that every body cell has, as seen in any school textbook. There's a nucleus, with chromosomes made of DNA, machinery for reading the genes on the chromosomes to make proteins, and the tiny bacteria-like bags called mitochondria that supply energy for the cell.

There are also various kinds of tubes and filaments, built up from proteins, which maintain the cell's shape and allow it to ferry chemicals from one place to another. The whole array is enclosed in a cell membrane, the all-important interface with everything outside.

Then there are the sticky-out bits that make a neuron look different from other cells, the neurites. The original simple view was that there are two clearly distinct types. Each neuron puts out an axon, for outgoing signals – nerve fibres are axons. The axon ends in a rounded terminal, almost but not quite touching another cell – usually another neuron. This is the synapse, a minute gap that the nerve signal has to cross to transfer information down the line.

▼ A massively branched set of dendrites drawn by microscopist Santiago Ramón y Cajal.

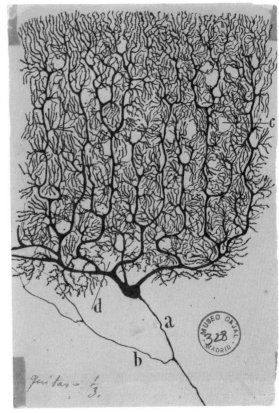

The other neurites are dendrites. Axons may branch, especially near the end, but dendrites typically divide over and over, hence the name (from the Greek for "tree"). They are recipients of axon signals, although axon terminals may also snuggle up to cell bodies. On dendrites, the nerve terminals either sit on the core of the dendrite or on smaller projections seen in some neurons, known as dendritic spines.

THE ULTIMATE NETWORK

You probably have the impression by now that the human brain is quite complex. It is down at the cellular level that this complexity really begins to hit home.

Neurons' axonal and dendritic feelers are a wonderfully flexible system. They produce hundreds, possibly thousands, of neural types, defined by their pattern of neurites, and adapted for different stations in the vast array of relays and transformers that add up to a nervous system. Some axons are short – from one neuron to a few neighbours – some long – from head to toes. Some link to a single synapse, some to multiple synapses, on the same or different dendrites. Dendrites form many different branch patterns, leading to names for neuron types: stellate, spindle, chandelier, candelabra, brush cell, cone cell, even "double bouquet".

The variations in connectivity are large so averages depend heavily on exactly where a sample of cells comes from. However, we can say that each axon can form connections with around 1,000 other neurons. Most connections are with cells close by, while around four in every hundred reach out to other parts of the brain. The total number of

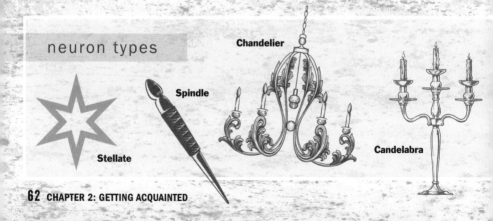

neuron types

Chandelier

Spindle

Stellate

Candelabra

synaptic connections in the brain is much larger than the total number of neurons. Estimates vary from 100 trillion (million million) to 1,000 trillion. If you still cannot remember where you put your car keys, it isn't because of lack of storage capacity, then.

There are other types of variation, too. Around four-fifths of all the genes in a mouse, which has about the same number as we do, are expressed in brain tissue. Not all will be active in every brain cell. Differences in gene expression, and hence protein manufacture, are large. Key genes expressed in neurons help with fine-tuning axonal and dendritic membranes, with making and disposing of neurotransmitters, and building the receptors that register the neurotransmitter when it is released,

▲ Neuronal interconnections are intricate, and constantly shifting.

or relay the signal inside the cell. All of these affect how messages are sent, and decoded, in the nervous system. We can probe small regions of the network in great detail nowadays, but the poetic phrase coined by the English physiologist Charles Sherrington still seems apt: "an enchanted loom where millions of flashing shuttles weave a dissolving pattern..."

Brush

Cone

Double bouquet

ONE AT A TIME

Researchers know better than anyone how overwhelmingly complex the whole network formed by brain cells is, so seek relief by considering them one at a time.

▲ *One day, miniature LEDs might be implanted to control light-sensitive neurons.*

Well, not quite singly. But certainly one small circuit at a time. One impressively precise technique allows experimenters to see individual cells in a neural circuit. Dubbed optogenetics, it builds on the genetic manipulation techniques used to install fluorescent proteins in cells (see Labelling with light, Chapter 1) to do something new – modifying neurons so that researchers can turn them on and off. It has been hailed as the most revolutionary technique in neuroscience of recent decades.

The trick is to engineer neurons to produce light sensitive proteins. The ones that work are known as opsins and are found in algae. They allow ions across cell membranes when they are exposed to light – the algae use them to sense the light and swim toward it. That means the protein has two states, and researchers have a switch. Instead of relying on information read out from the brain, as happens in the many scanning techniques, they can put information *into* the brain, and observe the results.

This works on neurons growing in a dish, and even on live creatures as long as the light can penetrate far enough into nervous tissue. Different proteins allow neurons to be activated, by blue light, or turned off, by yellow light, as desired. One of the first successful experiments controlled just a dozen neurons selected from the 100,000 or so in the brain of a fruit fly.

Arranged just right, these new switches can be used to test ideas about how particular neurons, or small groups of neurons, affect behaviour (see Chapter 12). Flies can be induced to take off, mice to start running around, or rodent memories to be reinforced or scrambled, all by light signals acting on engineered neurons in just the right place.

The technique involves use of genetically modified viruses so is not applicable to humans. If some other way is found to introduce the light-sensitive proteins, there are hopes of exploiting findings in mice that relate to recovery from spinal cord injuries and even neuron action in depression. Clinical application is still some way off, though.

◀ Lab mice with genetic modification of carefully selected neurons can be induced to run around with light signals.

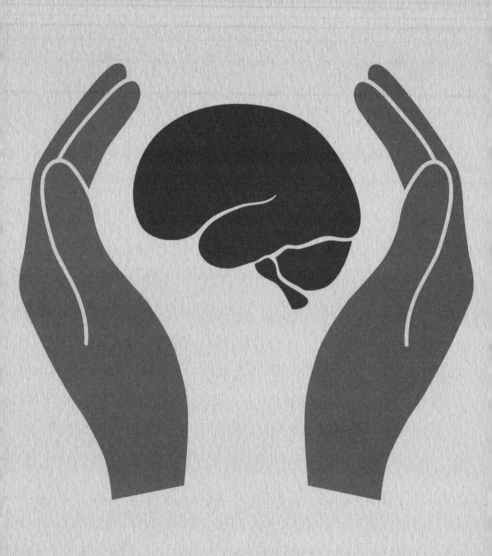

CHAPTER 3

LIFE WITH A BRAIN

BRAINS, WHO NEEDS THEM?

What are brains for, anyway? Some organisms do without them. Single-celled types have no choice, but there are plenty of multicellular organisms without specialized nerve cells. Take a look at the plants in the nearest garden.

Plants stay in one place, and there does seem to be a link between moving around and the use of a nervous system. It shows clearly in the sea squirt. The larvae of this spongy creature look a bit like tadpoles wriggling through the water. Their motion is coordinated by a simple nervous system, including an eye, a cord of nerves and a cerebral ganglion – a clump of neurons that serves as a mini-brain. After dispersing, the larvae select a spot on the seabed. They stay rooted for the rest of their lives, feeding on plankton they filter from the water. Apparently they have no further need for their "brains". Eye, cord and ganglion are reabsorbed into the adult creature.

◀▼ *A free-swimming sea squirt, and cluster of mature sea squirts, now immobile.*

The larval stage reveals the sea squirt as a more sophisticated creature that has adopted a simpler way to live as an adult. But how did those small patches of nervous tissue arise in the first place?

Brain evolution has to be approached indirectly. Skulls fossilize; soft brains don't. Reconstructing the origins of neurons and their circuitry relies heavily on studying life as we now know it, and working out which earlier forms present-day creatures resemble. That can mislead, but we can at least see that there are simple creatures with simple nervous systems, and a path by which they may have evolved.

That path starts under the sea, somewhere between the sponge and a group that includes jellyfish and sea anemones. Sponges are colonies of cells but have no neurons. Jellyfish have a nerve net: not yet a nervous system but a scattered collection of neuron-like cells. Presumably they always did, so nerve nets have been around for perhaps 550 million years at least. That's a long span but still around 3,000 million years shorter than the history of life on Earth.

▶ Box jellyfish: not brainy, but well networked.

A DIFFERENT SYMMETRY

The nerve net is proving more capable than biologists knew until recently. It can tie sensory cues to actions, as when a jellyfish dives to avoid less salty water. One species of box jellyfish even has eyes that help it navigate. But nervous systems more like ours, and more complex behaviour, go with a big change in body plan. Jellyfish and the like have radial symmetry. Brains, right up to the two hemispheres of our own bulging cortex, are bilateral.

Part of the history of nervous systems leads to creatures we now see that are as varied as worms, molluscs (slugs, snails and shellfish) and the cephalopods  (cuttlefish, squid and octopods) – some of which are pretty smart. They have their own complex evolutionary paths. So do the nematodes and arthropods – insects, spiders, crustaceans and all. All these species contribute to the large project of comparative neuroanatomy. But here we'll focus on the vertebrates. They combine bilateral symmetry with a nervous system whose organization looks familiar: a central nerve channel that links parts of the body to an outgrowth of neurons at one end. That basic plan goes back 500 million years.

Present-day fish, amphibians, reptiles, birds and mammals are all built this way. Their brains get gradually larger and more complex, until we arrive at the primates. No one thing drove this long train of development. But the evidence does suggest a strong factor that moved natural selection in the direction of more agile brains. Achieving motion allows a creature to go where the food is. That includes pursuit of prey. The simplest species in a world with predators benefits from acquiring cells that can sense when other

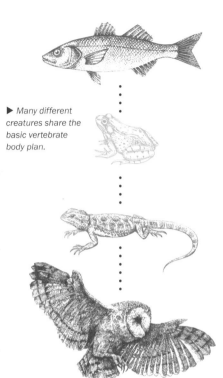

▶ Many different creatures share the basic vertebrate body plan.

creatures are near enough to present a danger.

We don't know that this is why the cells that began the journey toward nervous systems, the protoneurons, were useful. But a close look at the evolutionary timing is suggestive. As a review in 2014 put it, "animals evolved spiking neurones soon after they started eating each other."

SMALL STEPS

Look at the various kinds of backboned creatures, and you can easily make a story about gradual development of the brain that culminates in the one in our own heads. One popular tale was that we have a three-part (or triune) brain – with a reptile-derived part in the basal ganglia of the forebrain, a not very bright mammal tacked on, and then a neocortex added as the crowning glory. They generated instincts, emotions and intelligence, respectively, according to this theory.

It's a mistaken idea for several reasons. All the parts of the brain interact continuously, and the supposedly "primitive" parts are involved in "higher" functions. More basically, it assumes that once a piece of brain is there, it stops evolving. But the components of brains coevolve continuously. Ours is no exception.

Even so, there is a history to the emergence of brains that neuroscience has to take into account. As mentioned, fossil skulls and analysis of still existing brains provide information about comparative anatomy and brain development. Researchers can now study evolution in great detail at the molecular level, too. There are signalling molecules, and proteins that form ion channels across cell membranes, present in bacteria, for example, and they have recognizable descendants in the systems that allow neurons to communicate.

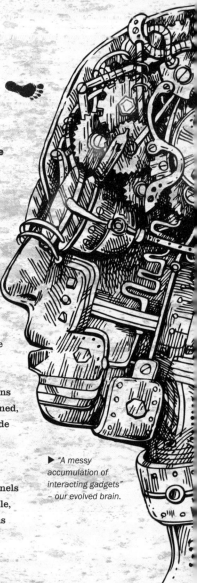

▶ *"A messy accumulation of interacting gadgets" – our evolved brain.*

All of this underlines one conclusion that resonates throughout neuroscience. Brains, including our own, were not designed like our machines. They evolved, just like any other organ.

That tells us something about how they are put together. Evolution works by trial and error, and the accumulation of small advantages. It does not automatically generate the best or most elegant solution to a problem. If natural selection was an engineer, it would be a tinkerer or a hacker, seeing what new things can be done by recombining existing parts, or by modifying them a little bit. As Francis Crick wrote in *The Astonishing Hypothesis*, if a new device works, in however odd a manner, evolution will try to promote it: "the final design may not be a clean one but rather a messy accumulation of interacting gadgets." It's not a particularly flattering picture of our brains, but it is a realistic one.

▼ *Evolution operates by trial and error. Science too, sometimes.*

SIZE DOES MATTER – A BIT

The simplest observation about brains is that some are larger than others – and they have got bigger over the span of evolution.

The size variation is impressive. In vertebrates, the smallest fishes and amphibians have brains that weigh a milligram, while a sperm whale's brain can reach 8kg (17lb 10oz).

That is not just because the whale is larger. One unusual dolphin, the false killer whale, has a brain just as big. Although body size accounts for most of the increase in brain size, some species have evolved a bigger brain than that would imply. An elephant's brain at a bit under 5kg (11lb) is a lot bigger than a human's, which averages 1.2kg (2lb 10oz). But our brain is roughly 2 per cent of our body weight, while an elephant's is only 0.1 per cent.

Closer to our own kind, chimps have larger brains for their size than gorillas. For fossils, we have to use volume measurements, which show an increase among our immediate forebears. The protohumans known as *Australopithecines*, who lived 3 to 4 million years ago, had brains occupying between 400cm³ and 450cm³ (24½–27½in³) around the same as a modern chimp. By 2 million years ago, *Homo habilis* had 700cm³ (42⅔in³) brains, and *Homo erectus* 1.8 million years ago probably reached 1,000cm³ (61in³).

So *Homo sapiens*, with a brain volume of 1,500cm³ (91½in³), got smart by growing a larger brain? It's not that simple. Recent fossil finds have complicated the story of human evolution – some small-brained specimens appear much later than previously supposed. And some parts of the brain have enlarged more than others. Most of the recent growth has clearly been in the cortex.

There are alterations in the thickness of the cortex to assess, too, and the density of neurons in the cortex varies across species. Humans score high on all these measures, with a large area of cortex (all those wrinkles), which is relatively thick (3mm/1⅛in, compared with just 1mm/³⁄₆₄in in dolphins), and lots of cells. Result, we have the most cortical neurons, perhaps 15 or 20 billion, of any land mammal, though at least one species of dolphin has more.

At any rate, intelligence does not correlate directly with brain size. Einstein's brain was 200g (7⅛oz) lighter than the human average.

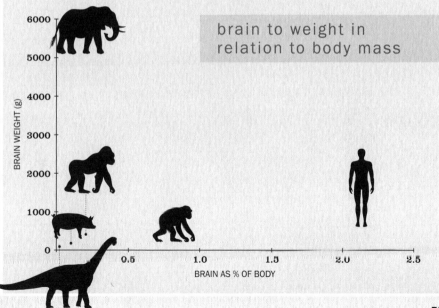

brain to weight in relation to body mass

BRAIN WEIGHT (g)

6000
5000
4000
3000
2000
1000
0

0.5   1.0   1.5   2.0   2.5

BRAIN AS % OF BODY

WHAT MAKES BRAINS SMART?

It's nice that we can look at something as complicated as the brain and see one obvious thing that ties in with the cognitive abilities that make humans stand out – the large volume and healthy crop of cells in our cerebral cortex. Can *that* account for what we think of as superior intelligence?

As we are a long way from unravelling the working of the cortex, let's lower the stakes a little with a different question. Can comparative brain anatomy tell us about the requirements for intelligence in general? Any answer depends on what we mean by intelligence. If other creatures have evolved brains that help them survive in new ways, we need a more general definition than just being the ape that talks. One useful species-neutral definition is being flexible, in

a way that generates new behaviour that can solve problems.

That grants intelligence of a kind to a select band of species. They include the octopus, whose brain is organized quite differently from ours (discussed in Chapter 11), some fish, social insects such as bees, one or two birds, especially parrots and crows, and mammals in general.

For all their differences, they have a few things in common, neuroanatomically speaking. They do have larger brains than less flexible, related species. They have identifiable brain regions with a lot of closely packed neurons that are highly interconnected. They also have parts, linked to the densely packed regions, that can work fast – because the distances between neurons, hence the length of axons, are short, and their axons conduct signals rapidly.

This is even true for a brain that looks vastly different from ours. Insects' tiny brains are highly developed ganglia that process visual input, and signals from their antennae. In social insects, the pair of structures known as the "mushroom bodies" has expanded and taken on processing all this information, and allows them to develop new tricks, and to navigate. Bees can even be trained in the lab, learning to move a small ball to secure a reward of sugar. Pretty clever for a creature with just 300,000 neurons to play with.

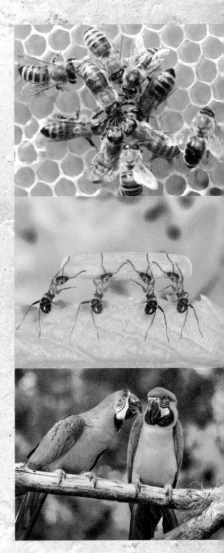

▶ *All these different creatures show intelligence, in their way.*

YOU ARE WHAT YOU EAT

The relatively large size of the human brain has prompted a catalogue of theories about what drove the increase. Complex social lives, hunting and butchering, tool use, language, even walking upright, have all been linked with evolution of our brains. But it's hard to know, in each case, which came first: a different brain or a new ability.

Theories based on more basic facts of life may be on firmer ground. Energy, and food to provide it, is a vital consideration. Here's the problem. Humans have larger brains than their close primate relatives. Our dense mass of neurons needs a lot of energy to run its ever-twinkling circuitry – 20 per cent of the human body's energy consumption at rest goes to the brain. Yet other primates are (mostly) herbivores. A gorilla spends most of its day chewing leaves. If it had a brain like ours, it would need an even larger intake, and a huge gut, to power it up. Yet the human gut actually got smaller while the brain enlarged. Was it something we ate?

◀ *Richard Wrangham accepts that not all foods need cooking.*

Meat-eating makes a difference. Using fire is even better, as the British primatologist Richard Wrangham, now at Harvard, has argued. Cooking makes digestion more efficient, so each meal delivers more calories. There are some issues with the timing: there is evidence that brains expanded before fire was definitely domesticated. But teeth certainly adapted to food that needed less chewing very early in the human lineage. It seems pretty likely that cooking helped us get smart.

Fire could also be a spur to cognitive development in other ways. Protohumans didn't live at fixed sites. They were roamers. Keeping a flame alive demands planning, getting fuel before the fire goes out. Food gathering had to happen alongside collecting enough wood to burn all night. Before fire-making was invented, fire had to be carried along with the troupe, with the embers shielded from rain. Anyone can warm their bones by the fire, so it prompts a keen interest in members of the group who are too lazy to fetch wood but still benefit from the heat. Building a way of living around fire calls forth a new level of sophistication in planning, cooperation, and social sensitivity, which all make new demands on the brain.

▶ A cooking pot over an open fire rests on complex social organization.

A DOMESTICATED BRAIN

The evidence that a large brain by itself is not the key to intelligence is strengthened by the fact that Neanderthal skulls, on average, housed larger brains than those of *Homo sapiens*. There's another relevant piece of the evolutionary story, too, a puzzling one.

Take a domesticated animal and compare its brain with the nearest wild equivalent. You have to allow for size, so let's choose an Alsatian and a wolf. The wolf's brain is almost 30 per cent larger.

This works for other domesticated animals, too – pigs and wild boar, say, or house cats and wild cats. It doesn't generalize completely because we have bred some creatures so single-mindedly

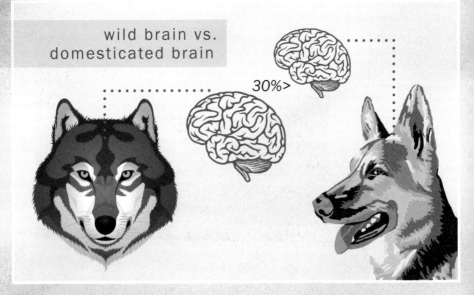

wild brain vs. domesticated brain

30%>

for size. We still end up with smaller-brained pigs, but intensively reared chickens, staggering under their unaccustomed body mass, actually have bigger brains than their wild ancestors.

Still, domestication generally reduces brain size. A curious fact that becomes more curious still when read against measurements from fossil humans. The human brain, evidence from around the world suggests, has also shrunk over the last 10,000–20,000 years.

Part of the reduction can again be linked to body size – we have also got smaller, on average, than our forebears. But how to account for the rest? Have we, too, been domesticated in some way?

There are similarities between animal domestication and recent human culture. A domesticated animal gets fed and is kept safe from predators. An agricultural settlement confers the same advantages on people, perhaps. On the other hand, subsistence agriculture often goes with malnourishment, which compromises brain growth.

Or perhaps our brains have shrunk because we have spared them other kinds of effort. The suggestion comes easily to mind in the age of the smartphone, although it's hard to think it through in the time of the first farmers. That pre-dates the origins of writing, for instance.

The human brain shrinkage may also reinforce the idea that it is the detailed internal working of the brain, not mere size, that confers intelligence.

And it provokes speculation about possible futures for us. The science fiction writer Kurt Vonnegut's novel *Galápagos* suggests that our brains are too big. Our descendants, a million years hence, have happily reverted to an aquatic life, with beaks, flippers, streamlined heads, and small brains.

A BRAIN IN EMBRYO

The story of brain development spans most of evolutionary history. It also begins anew each time a fertilized egg begins to grow into a new human. What follows is similar in all vertebrates, and has been studied in great detail. Here's how it goes.

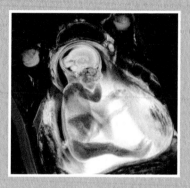

The embryo begins as a ball of cells, which divide as the embryo grows. After a few weeks, the cells move into layers. One region of the outermost layer thickens and folds in on itself to form a groove, and then a separate tube. This is the structure which develops into the brain and spinal cord. The hollow, fluid-filled tube develops into the ventricles of the fully-formed brain. The whole process is beautifully complex, but one way to look at it is

▲ *The growing brain shows clearly on this MRI scan of a foetus at eight months.*

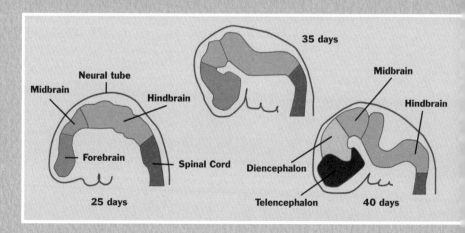

35 days

Midbrain

Neural tube

Midbrain

Hindbrain

Hindbrain

Forebrain

Spinal Cord

Diencephalon

Telencephalon

25 days

40 days

that the various parts of the brain arise from outgrowths of the ventricle walls. Within two months, the growing human embryo is equipped with budding growths of forebrain, midbrain and hindbrain and a month later it has an identifiable cerebrum.

Embryonic development relies on precision movements of cells, with some migrating quite long distances to their final destination. A striking example is the development of the cerebral cortex. This is destined to have six layers. All of the cells are formed from stem cells near the underlying ventricle, and then climb upward to the correct layer. Their migration can take more than two weeks. Glial cells build a scaffolding of fibres that neurons can follow. Chemical signals ensure they move in the right direction, past layers already in place. Some signals, such as a large molecule called Reelin secreted by the outer layer of neurons, have been identified. Mice lacking Reelin have a scrambled cortex, and a peculiar "reeling" gait.

The cortical cells migrating are mainly neurons, lots of them. The growing human foetus can make 250,000 neurons a minute. Almost all the neurons the fully-developed brain will ever have arise in the embryo. When they have all emerged, the human brain hasn't finished growing, but the skull is as large as it can be and still pass through the pelvic girdle. Time to be born.

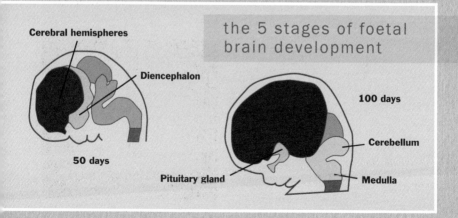

the 5 stages of foetal brain development

Cerebral hemispheres

Diencephalon

50 days

100 days

Cerebellum

Pituitary gland

Medulla

A BRAIN IS BORN

The swollen human cortex dictates an early birth but development continues long afterward. The newborn's brain is a seething mass of neurons. Nine months' growth has created a multitude of synaptic connections, too. Long tracts of nerves in white matter link different parts of the brain. Like neuronal migration, axon growth is guided by complex signalling arrangements so the axons' terminals end up in the right place. But there hasn't been time yet to organize the brain's fine structure.

Now the neurons must negotiate their role in the future brain. They are already connected because if a neuron doesn't form any nerve links with other cells it is programmed to die. In fact, neurons are so eager to make synapses that they generate more than the brain can use. Many more connections are formed immediately after birth, and the number reaches its maximum in most parts of the brain during the first year of the baby's life. A one-year-old has roughly twice as many synapses as an adult. After that, formation of new synapses continues, but the total

white matter development

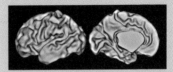

32 weeks

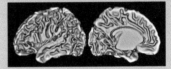

36 weeks

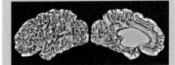

40 weeks

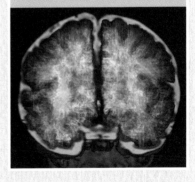

number begins to fall as unwanted connections are pruned by glial cells.

The basic architecture of the brain has followed the plans laid down in the genes. They influence which types of neurons grow, their destinations, and the principal pathways for signal traffic between brain regions. The long, slow fine-tuning that follows is more strongly shaped by experience. A baby, and a brain, out in the world is bombarded with sensory information – light, colour, movement, sound, touch, taste, smell, heat and cold – that could only be felt faintly, or not at all, in the womb.

There begins the lifelong process of arranging, rearranging and pruning synaptic connections that underlies learning, memory and understanding (see Chapters 5–8). All the while, the brain is growing, as it adds more nerve-rich white matter, and glial cells. A newborn baby's brain weighs well under 0.5kg (17⅔oz), around the same size as that of a newborn chimp. But the human baby's brain grows very fast, reaching more than half its adult weight in three months and tripling in weight by age four.

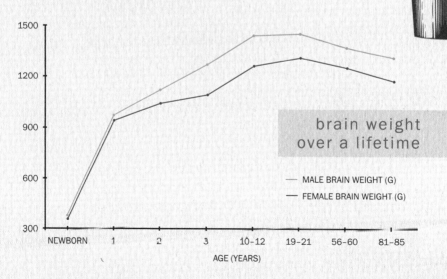

brain weight over a lifetime

— MALE BRAIN WEIGHT (G)
— FEMALE BRAIN WEIGHT (G)

AGE (YEARS)

▼ *Best foot forward, but only when the cerebellum has developed fully.*

CRITICAL LEARNING

A newborn mouse has never felt something brush its long whiskers. Rodents are nocturnal, and the mouse is born with a big cluster of neurons (known as the barrel cortex) wired to each individual whisker to collect vital sensory information. Leave the whiskers alone, and the relevant neurons learn to process the input. If they are clipped after birth, though, that doesn't happen and the mice never learn to use their whiskers properly. Clipping later does not have this effect. Rather, in adult mice, removing a whisker or two stimulates the barrel cortex to rewire neurons to serve the remaining whiskers.

There is a lot of brain to organize, probably too much for it to happen all at once. As anyone who has spent time with an infant knows, things happen in stages. The growth of the brain reflects this. The cerebellum, which is crucial for controlling movement, doubles in size in the months after birth. The hippocampus, involved in memory, increases more slowly.

Human and animal studies have established that environmental cues are needed for many brain-dependent abilities to develop properly. Some are programmed, to the extent that the cues must come at the right time. The mouse barrel cortex is a good model of a brain region that has a critical period for development.

An important human example is in vision. Visual acuity and depth perception are both affected if a child has one "lazy eye", which does not focus well or look in the right direction. If the condition is corrected early, their eyesight develops fully. If it isn't spotted before the age of five or six, this is less likely.

Some aspects of language learning show critical periods, too. It is really hard for most people to speak a second language learned as a teenager without an accent.

Overall, the brain remains adaptable, though. Making and unmaking connections continues throughout life, although learning a completely new subject – neuroscience for instance – gets more challenging with age.

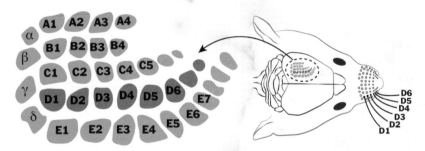

▲▶ The mouse's brain develops a map of its whiskers, that helps it learn how to navigate small spaces.

BOY BRAINS, GIRL BRAINS

Do male and female brains develop differently? Studies that suggest this appear from time to time, but assessing them is tricky. Here are some findings that appear well founded.

Women do have smaller brains than men, on average – because they have smaller bodies. Sex hormones, which affect embryonic development and trigger differentiation between males and females, also affect the brain. But any longer-term anatomical and behavioural effects that follow are hard to separate out from social and environmental influences on an easily influenced organ.

There *are* clear examples of differences in particular brain regions between males and females in other species. In songbirds for instance, in the spring males serenade females, not vice versa, and they have an enlargement in one region to help them learn the new songs they acquire each year. This, biologically speaking, counts as *sexual dimorphism*, in which there are two distinct states that divide cleanly between the sexes. That is different from sex differences, where they exist, which are averages derived from populations where the sexes overlap on some measure.

The two shouldn't be confused, as often happens in discussions of "male" and "female" brains. The few good examples of differences in brain anatomy are statistical. There's a particular nucleus of the human hypothalamus, for instance, that is roughly twice the size in men than it tends to be in women, on average. Still, a third of men have nuclei that are "female" sized.

More importantly, although there are differences between categories of people however they are grouped, in most respects human brains are all alike. As authors of one overview put it in 2016, "human brains are better described as belonging to a single heterogeneous population rather than two distinct populations."

Critics of overblown claims about differences between male and female brains say the topic is rife with "neurosexism". On the other hand, there was a need for a corrective to an assumption embodied in many neuroscience studies – that studying the male brain can tell you everything you need to know.

▼ Male brains are larger, on average, than females, but only because their bodies are, too.

CONNECTIVITY, HEMISPHERES AND HYPE

A study published at the end of 2013 in the prestigious *Proceedings of the National Academy of Sciences* in the USA presented results of a survey of pathways in nearly 1,000 brains using the new magnetic resonance imaging (MRI) technique called diffusion tensor imaging. This registers movement of water molecules, which tend to track along nerve fibres and so can reveal nerve connections.

The results, according to the researchers, showed distinct differences in male and female brains – amounting to distinct connectomes. Male brains had greater connectivity between front and rear of the brain within each hemisphere compared with females. Conversely, females had more connections *between* hemispheres.

The difference was statistical, but established – the authors said – "fundamental differences in the structural architecture of the human brain". Specifically, they reckoned that "male brains are structured to facilitate connectivity between perception and coordinated action, whereas female brains are designed to facilitate communication between

▶ An image summarizing data from many scans that indicates pathways of stronger connection between regions in the front and rear of the brain, on average, in male subjects.

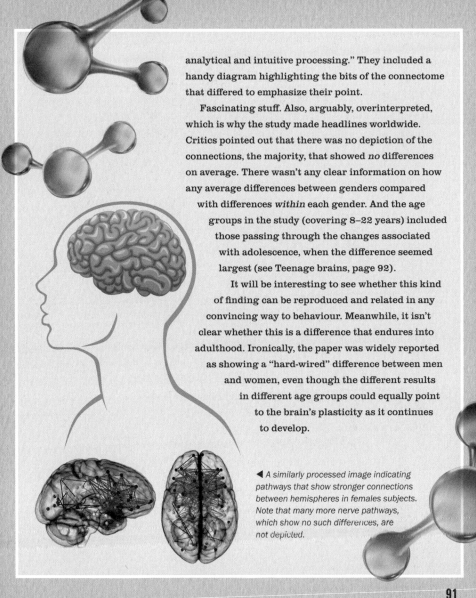

analytical and intuitive processing." They included a handy diagram highlighting the bits of the connectome that differed to emphasize their point.

Fascinating stuff. Also, arguably, overinterpreted, which is why the study made headlines worldwide. Critics pointed out that there was no depiction of the connections, the majority, that showed *no* differences on average. There wasn't any clear information on how any average differences between genders compared with differences *within* each gender. And the age groups in the study (covering 8–22 years) included those passing through the changes associated with adolescence, when the difference seemed largest (see Teenage brains, page 92).

It will be interesting to see whether this kind of finding can be reproduced and related in any convincing way to behaviour. Meanwhile, it isn't clear whether this is a difference that endures into adulthood. Ironically, the paper was widely reported as showing a "hard-wired" difference between men and women, even though the different results in different age groups could equally point to the brain's plasticity as it continues to develop.

◄ *A similarly processed image indicating pathways that show stronger connections between hemispheres in females subjects. Note that many more nerve pathways, which show no such differences, are not depicted.*

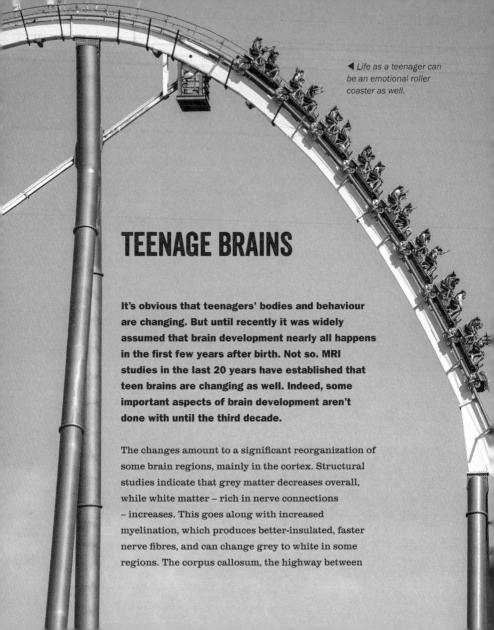

◄ *Life as a teenager can be an emotional roller coaster as well.*

TEENAGE BRAINS

It's obvious that teenagers' bodies and behaviour are changing. But until recently it was widely assumed that brain development nearly all happens in the first few years after birth. Not so. MRI studies in the last 20 years have established that teen brains are changing as well. Indeed, some important aspects of brain development aren't done with until the third decade.

The changes amount to a significant reorganization of some brain regions, mainly in the cortex. Structural studies indicate that grey matter decreases overall, while white matter – rich in nerve connections – increases. This goes along with increased myelination, which produces better-insulated, faster nerve fibres, and can change grey to white in some regions. The corpus callosum, the highway between hemispheres, thickens. At the micro-level, beyond the reach of scanners, there is evidence that dendrites are bushier, with more branches.

All this goes along with subtler changes, including more synaptic pruning. The readjustments of brain wiring take years, beginning toward the rear of the brain and moving slowly toward the front.

Functional MRI also suggests that teenagers draw on different brain regions for some tasks. For example, the medial prefrontal cortex appears more active in adolescents when they think about other people's minds than it does in adults. This doesn't mean that they cannot understand others' intentions so well, but may indicate that they do it differently. This fits with the suggestion by British researcher Sarah-Jayne Blakemore that teens' brains are undergoing adjustments relevant to aspects of social life where adult competence takes time to appear.

As ever, the fine details of links between brain structure and behaviour

▲ Teens may take risks that older brains judge unacceptable.

are mostly unclear. But there's enough evidence about the larger scales to speculate that the ability to reason clearly and consider consequences is still developing in adolescence, and that the state of brain development in teenagers ties in with their social sensitivity, appetite for risk, and the emotional turmoil that at least some people undergo. If that's how you remember the teen years, consider it a sign that your brain was busy moving toward a more adult formation.

MATURITY

There is no qualification certificate issued for a finished brain. It goes on changing as we age, though more gradually. The reduction in childhood grey matter that began in the teenage years (cortical thinning) goes on into the early twenties, sometimes later. White matter volume, signifying connectivity, goes on increasing into the fourth decade in some people.

▲ *New learning, new skills and new neural connections go together.*

As long as the brain remains active, and it must remain active, it continues to change. Synaptic connections are made and unmade as memories form, and learning new tasks modifies neural networks (see Chapter 7). We may get set in our ways, but we can alter our habits and acquire new skills with persistence. Changing how we think and behave takes time because, we believe, it eventually leads to changes in synapses. And injuries, such as those from a stroke, can lead to substantial reorganization and sometimes recovery of lost abilities, usually over even longer periods.

NO MORE NEURONS?

Brain connections change, but after infancy we have to work with the neurons we've been given. So it was believed for most of the last century.

Now the picture is more complicated. In the 1970s it was reported that birds such as canaries make new neurons each year in the part of the brain that learns a new song. Then fresh neurons were spotted appearing in adult rats and monkeys. The clincher was work in the 1990s that found stem cells in adult rats that resemble those found in the embryonic brain and can make new neurons.

Humans have such cells, too, and most researchers now think that we make new neurons all the time. We shouldn't get too excited about it yet. The numbers are small – maybe a few hundred a day in the hippocampus, for example. What they do is not yet clear, though it is nice to know the possibility of refreshing our stock of brain cells exists.

In the future, it might offer the prospect of stimulating, or perhaps transplanting, stem cells to help repair brain injuries. However, as in other areas where there is speculation about harnessing stem cells, we do not understand very well how to activate them reliably, nor, equally important, how to turn them off again once they begin reproducing.

◀ Bird-brained perhaps, but they can generate new neurons.

AGEING BRAINS

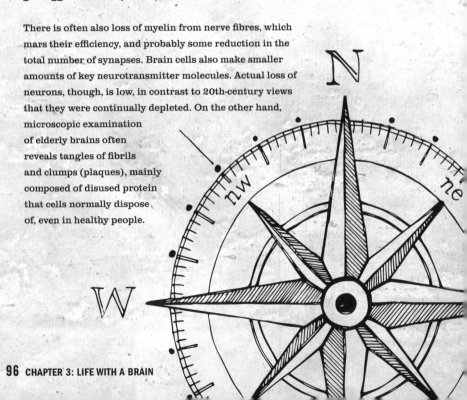

There are physical changes, most clearly a gradual reduction in volume, as our brains get older – although the loss normally only reaches around 10 per cent in a 90-year-old. The ventricles get bigger to take up the space.

There is often also loss of myelin from nerve fibres, which mars their efficiency, and probably some reduction in the total number of synapses. Brain cells also make smaller amounts of key neurotransmitter molecules. Actual loss of neurons, though, is low, in contrast to 20th-century views that they were continually depleted. On the other hand, microscopic examination of elderly brains often reveals tangles of fibrils and clumps (plaques), mainly composed of disused protein that cells normally dispose of, even in healthy people.

Any or all of these gradual changes may account for the reductions in performance that are popularly associated with ageing. These include:

* Difficulties with memory – both recalling stored information and committing new things to memory;
* Slower response to some cognitive demands, including following long chains of reasoning and managing attention when several different things are going on.

That relates to multitasking, although there is debate about the extent to which genuine multitasking is possible at any age. It may just involve rapid switching of attention back and forth between single tasks.

Although these changes may occur, they are far from universal. Around 20 per cent of people aged 70 can match 20-year-olds' brains on cognitive tests.

Research continues on how to maximize the chances of being in that 20 per cent. So far, there is no magic formula, but there are two general conclusions that go a little beyond standard advice on how to prolong good health. Maintaining a rich social network is beneficial for the ageing brain, and so is keeping up regular exercise – both physical and mental. To make things easier, one recent study suggested that the rhythmic forces generated by one simple activity are especially beneficial for cerebral blood flow. The activity in question? Walking.

E

Spanish club
7.30 at the old
town hall

Elizabeth's
birthday is ne,
Wednesday

Dry cleaning
ready Friday
afternoon

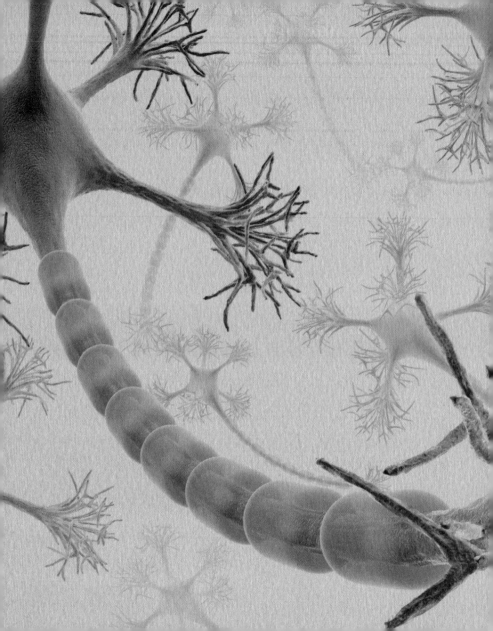

CHAPTER 4

A VERY SPECIAL CELL

WHAT WE KNOW ABOUT NEURONS

Look at the structure of the brain. Zoom in to the level of neurons. Here's where the complexity of neuroscience's target may begin to overwhelm the casual observer. Sure, the brain is complicated. But every one of the cells that make it all possible seems almost a mini-brain in itself. Understanding how it works demands going down to the level of molecules, where biology shades into chemistry, then into physics. We'll catch some glimpses of that in this chapter, before zooming out again.

It helps to begin with the bare essentials. A neuron is a cell that can send and receive signals through a network. There are many kinds, but the simplest one is a bipolar neuron, found in the sensory system. You can think of it as having an input cable – a dendrite – receiving signals from the sensing organ at one end, and an output cable – an axon – at the other.

An active neuron sends electrical pulses down the axon. Each pulse is the same, but the more active the cell, the more frequent they are. The increase above the background rate, and probably the pattern of pulses, registers with the next cell. The excited neuron can "fire" up to 1,000 times

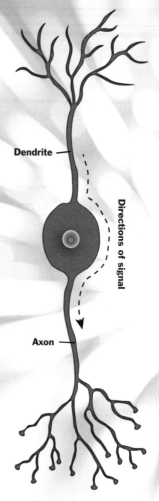

Dendrite

Directions of signal

Axon

▲ *A typical bipolar neuron, one of the simplest types.*

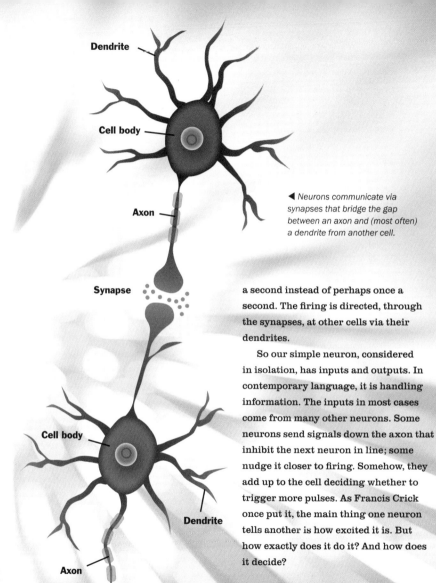

Dendrite

Cell body

Axon

Synapse

◀ *Neurons communicate via synapses that bridge the gap between an axon and (most often) a dendrite from another cell.*

Cell body

Dendrite

Axon

a second instead of perhaps once a second. The firing is directed, through the synapses, at other cells via their dendrites.

So our simple neuron, considered in isolation, has inputs and outputs. In contemporary language, it is handling information. The inputs in most cases come from many other neurons. Some neurons send signals down the axon that inhibit the next neuron in line; some nudge it closer to firing. Somehow, they add up to the cell deciding whether to trigger more pulses. As Francis Crick once put it, the main thing one neuron tells another is how excited it is. But how exactly does it do it? And how does it decide?

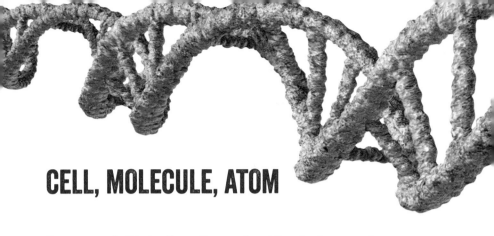

CELL, MOLECULE, ATOM

Neurons can do things other cells cannot, and theories in neuroscience begin with these beautiful scraps of life. The drawings Cajal made a century ago are wonderfully detailed (see page 21) but only hint at their special qualities. Much more has been uncovered at the level of molecules.

Researchers must plumb deeper layers of organization to refine ideas about what brains as a whole can do. They may not need to go all the way down, into the microworlds where quantum mechanical effects dominate, to dissect neuronal interactions (athough the mathematical physicist Roger Penrose disagrees – see page 282). But they must tease out events involving molecules, and atoms.

There are a *lot* of molecules in a cell. Let's simplify the collection, guided by modern molecular biology. Crudely, there are big molecules and small ones. The big molecules – sometimes very big – do stuff. These are the proteins.

They are made from smaller molecules joined together in order, as the linear information in another big molecule, DNA, instructs. Some other very large molecules are involved in making the proteins, in neurons as elsewhere.

Proteins have that linear sequence, a daisy chain of amino acids. But they fold up into three-dimensional shapes. Most important things in cells depend on one of those shapes fitting some other molecule. It can be another big one, giving it a special molecular nudge or helping build a larger structure. Or it might be one of the small ones. Sometimes the small molecule is changed

▶ *DNA, the famous double helix, is one of the largest cellular molecules of all.*

by the protein. Then we have an enzyme that catalyses a chemical reaction. Sometimes the protein is changed by the small molecule, because its folding alters slightly when it finds the right one. Then we have a possible component of a signalling system. Especially clever proteins sometimes do both.

Imagine all this as an enormous collection of floppy locks, and bendy keys, mixed in a soup, constantly bumping into each other at speed. A molecule does not know whether it is a hormone or a neurotransmitter (or both), an enzyme, a bit of cellular scaffolding, or an internal messenger. It just does its thing. Somehow, neurons promote the right kind of molecular encounters to do their special work. Most of it depends on one special part of the cell, the membrane.

▶ *Molecules jostle randomly inside the cell, sometimes finding a companion that fits.*

103

TWO SIDES TO EVERYTHING

It's not just soup in there. Cells use membranes to organize the space inside, and to mark their own boundaries. Neuronal outer membranes have unique properties. Understanding why involves a little more molecular biology. The membrane is a double layer of fatty molecules that surrounds the entire cell: body, axon, dendrites and all. Those particular molecules have water-loving ends, which line up facing the watery insides of the cell or the equally watery outside, and water-hating ends, which hide inside the membrane. This means that, while immeasurably thin, it has clearly defined regions.

Those regions orient proteins that sit inside the membrane. They know which way is up. The whole array is semi-fluid and studded with special proteins that "float" in the membrane layer.

That describes any cell membrane. The proteins transform the membrane from a passive barrier to one that allows just the right traffic between the inside and outside of the cell. Neurons are cellular high achievers because their membrane proteins regulate the traffic more thoughtfully.

They do it the way proteins do anything, by being the right shape, and sometimes changing shape. There are many different ones in the neuronal membrane. Researchers have worked out

the structures of quite a few, so we know the basic types.

For physical transport there are pores and pumps. A protein molecule, or a bunch of them clinging together, forms a hole in the membrane that allows small things through. Some pores are highly selective – allowing one kind of metal ion, say, to pass. Some only work one way. Some, crucially, can open or close. And some proteins can pump a particular molecule in or out to maintain a difference in concentration across the membrane.

There's another kind of membrane transfer as well: information. A protein, usually one sticking out of the cell, clasps a small molecule that comes

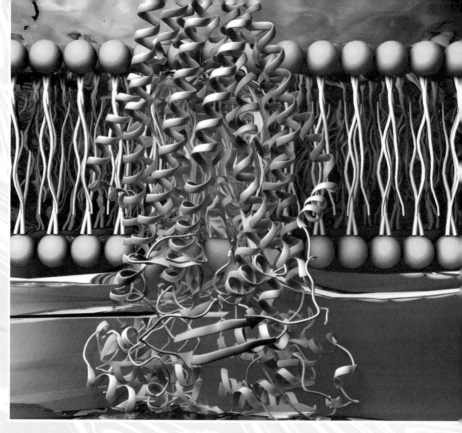

▲ A model of a large protein, depicted in mauve showing the twists and turns of its backbone, of the kind that move ions or small molecules across cell membranes. The blue globes are the water loving ends of the molecules that form the two-layer membrane.

within reach. Then it snaps into a different shape all along its length, so that a region inside the cell alters too. Nothing physical has crossed over. But a protein receptor has registered a chemical signal from outside, and shown a response inside.

EXCITING TIMES – THE NERVE IMPULSE

When a neuron is excited, it fires. An electrical signal shoots down the axon. Not, as you might guess, like electrons down a conducting wire. The signal is a change in voltage that sweeps along the axon membrane, passed on by the action of some of those special proteins.

What they do was proposed long before they were identified, when Hodgkin and Huxley plotted how the nerve impulse works by recording electrical pulses inside the axon of a squid (see page 29). The membrane at rest has a small excess of positive charge outside. That creates an electrical potential difference – measured in millivolts – across the fatty barrier, which is negatively charged inside.

Reduce that difference a little near one end of the axon, and nothing happens. Reduce it a bit more, and the neuron fires. The voltage difference flips completely, to negative outside, positive inside, then almost as quickly flips back again, before returning to the resting potential, as it is known.

Voltage recording in the squid showed these changes went with surges of positive ions, charged atoms of metals, from one side of the membrane to the other. Sodium ions enter the cell. Then potassium ions leave it.

Hodgkin and Huxley predicted that there must be specific ion channels in the membrane that can open and close. Half a century on, and those channels have been identified – specific protein molecules respond to changes in voltage to begin the axon spike, then close it down. The back-and-forth voltage change is triggered at the beginning of the axon, then moves along it. Separate proteins furnish the ion pumps that maintain the resting potential.

The whole process is a small electrical shudder. It has also been compared to the snap of a skipping rope, or the burning of a sparkler. But it is probably best to think of the action potential, as the whole cycle is known, as its own thing. This sparkle is over in milliseconds, and the neuron can fire again milliseconds later.

action potential graph

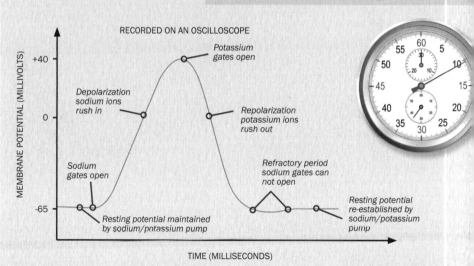

RECORDED ON AN OSCILLOSCOPE

MEMBRANE POTENTIAL (MILLIVOLTS)

+40

0

-65

Potassium gates open

Depolarization sodium ions rush in

Repolarization potassium ions rush out

Sodium gates open

Resting potential maintained by sodium/potassium pump

Refractory period sodium gates can not open

Resting potential re-established by sodium/potassium pump

TIME (MILLISECONDS)

END OF THE LINE – THE SYNAPSE

An axon can be short, connecting two neurons in the same part of the brain, or as long as you like. The longest in humans reaches from the brainstem to the toes, so might reach 2m (6½ft). The similar nerve fibre in a blue whale may be 25m (82ft) long, and can grow 3cm (1¼in) in a day.

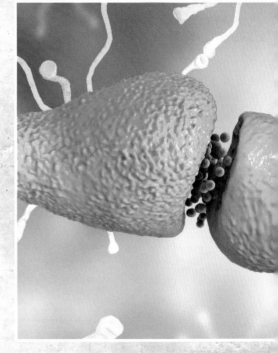

▼ The electrical nerve signal is converted into chemicals, which diffuse across a minute gap at the synapse.

But however long, every axon stops short of the next cell. So does the nerve impulse. But the signal travels on, via the synapse.

An axon or its branch comes to an end a tiny distance away from a specialized region of membrane in the next cell – on a dendrite, a dendritic spine or sometimes the cell body. The end of the axon is packed with small bags of chemicals, some of which release their contents when an action potential hits. The chemical – a neurotransmitter – diffuses rapidly across the gap between cells, a mere 20 nanometres (billionths of a metre), and is recognized by receptor proteins on the post-synaptic membrane. An electrical signal has been converted into a chemical message.

SOUP OR SPARKS?

Seeing the synaptic cleft in the electron microscope did away with one of the great controversies of neuroscience, which began with the disagreement between Cajal and Golgi about whether neurons were bounded cells or a single net.

A related controversy about the cell–cell signal was more or less resolved a little earlier. Did the brain work via soup or sparks? When action potentials were first recorded, it

▲ *Otto Loewi.*

seemed that electricity ruled. But chemical advocates worked on until a moment of discovery in 1921 that confirms the brain works in mysterious ways.

Otto Loewi in Austria isolated a beating frog heart in culture, and stimulated the nerve that slows a frog's pulse. Then he tried an idea that came to him in a dream. A scribbled note he wrote in the middle of the night was no help, but the next night he got it down legibly. Would a sample of fluid from around that heart slow a second one? It did. Something in the solution must be responsible.

With a lot more work, he was able to show that the something was acetylcholine – the first neurotransmitter to be identified.

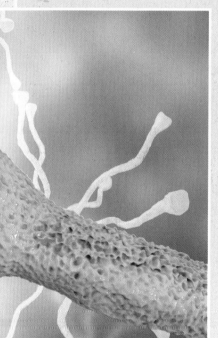

ONE ACTION POTENTIAL, MANY OUTPUTS

Biology loves exceptions, and axonal connections are also found without chemical synapses, but where an electrical signal passes from cell to cell directly via a so-called gap junction. But the vast majority avoid this neat, efficient, arrangement. Why?

All the neuron can do with its electrical signal is send it more or less frequently. But the action potential can send many different signals thanks to variations in the chemical synapse.

Modern neuroscience has compiled a large catalogue of neurotransmitters. Some act on one of many different receptors linked to ion channels. If the channel opens and allows positive ions into the post-synaptic neuron, it shifts it nearer to firing. It is excitatory. If the channel allows in negative ions, it is inhibitory.

Glutamate, an amino acid – and so a small molecule that has been around as long as cellular life – is the most commonly used excitatory

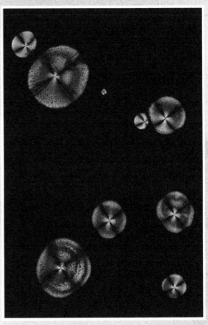

▲ *Crystals of pure glutamate.*

neurotransmitter. Inhibition is the job of two other amino acids, gamma-aminobutyric acid (GABA) and glycine.

More complex effects are achieved via other receptors, which recognize a neurotransmitter, alter their shape, and trigger further changes inside the receiving neuron. They are linked into chains of cause and effect that can control many events inside the cell. Some activate enzymes. Some even alter gene expression. The main class are coupled to a protein, known as G-protein. Different G-protein receptors respond to neurotransmitters that are all chemically amines – including acetylcholine, dopamine and a handful of others. More recently, a third class of neurotransmitters have been isolated, which are larger peptide molecules. There are at least 100 different ones, and counting.

So the basic model synapse can have a host of accessories for fine adjustment of the signal. The many classes of synapse are the most developed example of the main feature of neurons. They work differently because the detailed geography of the proteins in their membranes can be extremely varied, between cells and in regions of the same cell. And a synapse, like a neuron,

Axon

Synaptic bouton

Synaptic vesicle

Release of neurotransmitter

Synaptic cleft

Neurotransmitter diffusing

Receptors

Dendrite

To cell body

◀ *Synapses have the same basic structure, many different neurotransmitters, and even more types of receptors on the dendritic membrane.*

is almost infinitely adjustable. As Chapter 7 explains, that informs our theories of memory and learning.

PUTTING SYNAPSES TOGETHER

If the arrangement of pores and pumps that allows nerve fibres to transmit a signal appeared all at once, it could only have been by magic. But some of the molecular bits and pieces were in use long before neurons, or synapses, evolved.

The action potential, for example, depends on proteins known as voltage gated ion channels. A pore opens across the cell membrane under the influence of a shift in voltage between the inside and outside of the cell. Present-day bacteria have proteins that do something very similar, probably because cells always needed a way to manage the flow of ions. Without that, a cell that concentrates ions takes up water and bursts.

Comparing protein sequences allows good guesses about some evolutionary relationships. Thus, the first ion channel was almost certainly tailored for potassium ions. Duplicating its genes allowed later mutations that made channels better adapted for sodium and calcium.

Recent work has exploited biochemists' ability to survey all the proteins in a sample. The complexity of the synapse, for instance, is shown by analysis of a region adjoining the membrane of the receiving cell, prosaically termed the post-synaptic density (PSD).

Until the 1970s, it was known simply as a blob in electron micrographs. We do not know its complete structure yet, but the PSD in a mouse, for example, contains more than 1,100

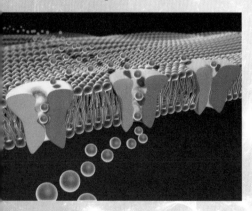

◀ *Ion channels in cell membranes help control intracellular pressure.*

▲ *A model of part of the potassium channel. This part of the protein helps join four identical pieces together, with a hollow pore in between them, forming the molecular passageway for metal ions.*

different proteins. Some hold the whole assembly in place. The rest are channels, receptors, enzymes, signalling molecules, and proteins involved in transport of other molecules. Managing the signal traffic across the synapse is obviously demanding.

A structure this fancy evolves in many small steps. This raises the intriguing possibility that more sophisticated brains rely on more elaborate synapses, and more complex arrangements at the PSD.

There is some evidence for this. Mice have more elaborate synaptic accessories than fruit flies. It seems likely that evolution of our brains involved more subtle changes than the increase in size of the cortex. We can speculate that changes in synaptic proteins give rise to new kinds of neurons, in more complex networks.

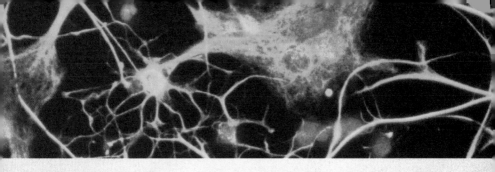

MANY INPUTS, ONE OUTPUT

▲ *The glial cells known as astroctyes play a role in modulating synapses that is still being explored.*

A look at the synapse is a reminder that neurons make connections. So let's put a single neuron back into the network. Even just one neuron immediately presents subtleties galore.

They revolve around the question: how does a neuron know when to fire? The axon generates an action potential in response to inputs from synapses. We can start one artificially with an electrode. And some things that affect inputs and outputs are clear. But precisely how the neurons in a living brain process a shifting set of inhibitory and excitatory inputs to produce a result remains elusive. Most theorists suggest that the neuron computes what to do from the sum of all the inputs, and that this is how it processes information. The metaphor seems appealing but does not tell you how it is done.

What is known is that there are lots of ways of weighting the inputs differently – modulating the signals the neuron is sensing. More are still being discovered. Here are a few.

The most important inputs are probably the direct ones from neurotransmitters that affect ion channels. Excitatory inputs open sodium channels, moving positive charge across the membrane and taking the cell closer to the voltage threshold for firing. Inhibitory inputs open channels for negative chloride ions, with the opposite effect. Neurotransmitters acting on these gated channels work fast.

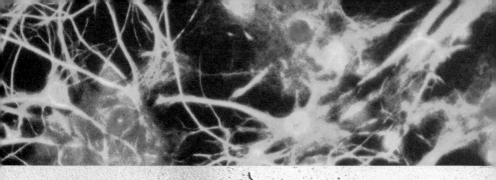

Then comes the modulation. Protein receptors that release chemical messengers in the cell can have many effects. Some involve different ion channels. Others affect enzymes, or even genes. Any of these changes can make the cell as a whole more or less excitable.

Another, poorly understood, kind of modulation comes from the dendrites. Dendrites can be relatively simple conductors of a synaptic input, but many neurons have more complex dendrites with their own specialized arrays of ion gates. Some can start small electrical signals of their own. Both can activate or inhibit a neuron. And astrocytes, the most common class of glial cells, make their own electrical and chemical contributions to the outcome.

All these interactions contribute to the millisecond-by-millisecond outcome: a neuron that produces a fresh action potential, or stays quiet. And trillions of those, somehow, add up to our moment-to-moment thoughts and feelings.

▼ *Dendrites, shown here in the cerebral cortex, differ widely in their configuration, and response to incoming signals from synapses.*

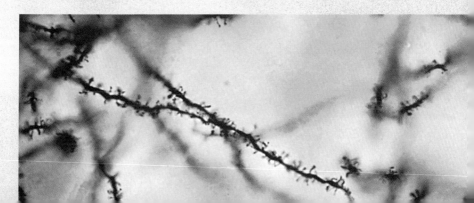

A NEURON'S REACH

A neuron Is a tiny cell, one among billions, emitting tiny electrical signals. But a single neuron can have a stunning network reach.

In physical distance, we have long known that a well-insulated axon can reach from the brain to the toes.

More significant is the sheer number of connections a neuron can make. This varies so much that average numbers are approximate – counting cells in a large volume is hard, never mind synapses. Some neurons have just a few connections, while the elaborately branched dendritic trees of Purkinje cells in the cortex can lead to 100,000 synapses. The total number of synapses is probably in the trillions. The heavy synaptic pruning during development does not mean the links are made randomly in the first place. There are subtle controls on the direction of axon growth, and where and when dendrites grow branches and spines, that are still under intensive investigation.

But let's think again about numbers. Suppose the average number of cells one imaginary representative neuron connects to is 10,000. Now let each of the 10,000 neurons connected to our first one connect to 10,000 others. (Occasionally, an axon branch reaches back and synapses with its own cell but not often enough to affect these numbers.) If there are no overlaps, we now have 100 million cells connected. If each of *those* cells makes 10,000 connections, we already have a total at least ten times the number of neurons in an average human brain – 100 billion, to cite the round figure that was generally accepted until recently.

The point is not that the real brain is like this. It isn't. But the capacity of neurons to grow networks means that, in principle, no single cell need be more than three steps from being linked, in however small a way, to the entire brain. Probing how neurons work always has to take account of this power to connect.

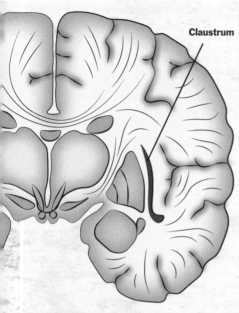

Claustrum

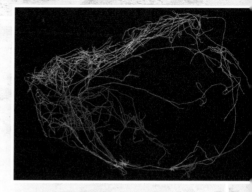

▲ A digital reconstruction, from green fluorescent protein microscopy, tracing all the connections the "crown of thorns" neuron makes around the mouse brain.

◀ A few neurons in the small region known as the claustrum have synaptic links with almost all the outer parts of the mouse brain.

A MISSING LINK?

Every neuron needs connections that suit the tasks it is involved with, some close, some far away. And mammal brains – well, mice at least – do have a neuron whose fibres can tap into the whole brain.

The cell in question is one of three whose connections are newly mapped and were reported at a scientific meeting in 2017. The trio of cells all have networks that extend over an unusual range of brain regions, in both hemispheres. One, dubbed the "crown of thorns", has pathways of connection that go round the outside of the entire brain.

Christof Koch of the Allen Institute in the USA, where the painstaking imaging of the neural pathways was done, points out that these neurons sit in a part of the brain, known as the claustrum, which he thinks is linked to consciousness (see Chapter 11). This far-reaching neuron may not be the key to the conscious self – in mouse or human – but certainly looks as if it must have some role in integrating information from different parts of the brain.

CHAPTER 5

WHAT'S HAPPENING?

SENSATIONAL

Perception, according to the British physiologist J Z Young, is "a search for information relevant for living". Our brains get that information through the senses. We can sense molecules, an ability shared with the simplest bacteria, via taste and smell. We can sense the air around us vibrating, as sound. We can sense photons via our visual system. And we can sense pressure and force, as touch through the skin and, internally, as an index of our body's position and motion.

All senses depend on specialized cells that have a way of registering the incoming information directly. One way or another, they alter electrical differences across membranes and trigger firing in a sensory neuron. Each sense thus converts the incoming information into the common code of the brain, an electrical input.

That part is quite well understood. The hard stuff comes in tracing how the networks that receive the sensory input process these initial signals. In the end, each will produce a representation of the world outside the brain. The long word there is important. What we see, to use the example that seems most often in the forefront of human consciousness, feels like a directly accessible vision of what is really out there. It isn't. It's a moment-to-moment construct, offered up after several stages of complex processing of many inputs. The result is a kind of working hypothesis. Normally, when we act on such hypotheses they turn out to be right. Senses evolved to convey information that increased an organism's chances of survival. So there is always a payoff from making a better approximation of some feature of reality. But it is still a hypothesis.

On top of those hypotheses our brains build more and more elaborate actions. But first they must gather information that allows a reasonably good guess about what we should be responding to.

THE LONG ROAD TO VISUALIZATION

As you read this, it feels as if there's a fixed vantage point behind your eyes from which you are conscious of the scene that includes these words. Neuroscience has a rather different story to tell. It has not (yet) revealed a specific location in the brain where the image is created. Rather, there is a lengthy sequence of transformations of signals from the eyes.

Consider the eye at some instant as scanning to generate a stream of data. Incoming light in the visual field is turned into electrical pulses in axons. Their information is processed in stages, each of which produces a new array of

neuronal signals presented to the next part of the visual system.

We know a good deal about some of these stages, which happen in different parts of the brain. Some occur in parallel, and isolate

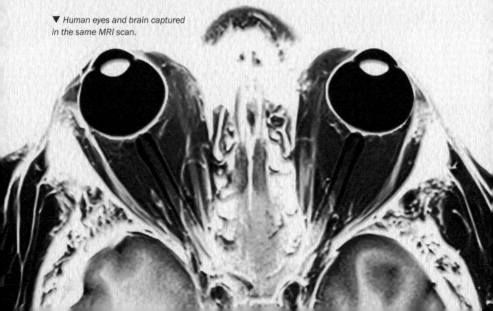

▼ *Human eyes and brain captured in the same MRI scan.*

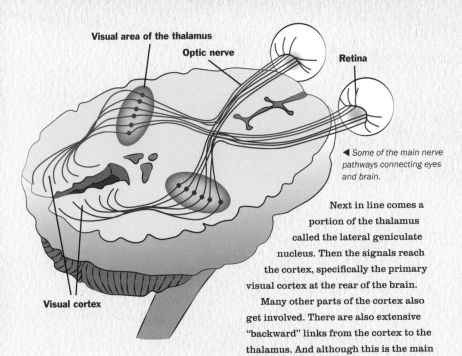

Visual area of the thalamus

Optic nerve

Retina

◀ *Some of the main nerve pathways connecting eyes and brain.*

Visual cortex

particular aspects of the image. Visual inputs are easy to control, and much research has linked specific inputs to recording from individual neurons, mainly in cats and monkeys.

The processing that turns a sea of visual stimuli into an image begins in the retina, which sends the first results out of the back of the eye via the optic nerves. They cross over, and each nerve bundle is sorted so that signals from one side of the visual field (from both eyes) pass to the opposite hemisphere.

Next in line comes a portion of the thalamus called the lateral geniculate nucleus. Then the signals reach the cortex, specifically the primary visual cortex at the rear of the brain.

Many other parts of the cortex also get involved. There are also extensive "backward" links from the cortex to the thalamus. And although this is the main route for visual processing, there are other subsidiary routes – important for registering day and night rhythms and controlling eye movements.

This is the most complex perceptual system in humans – as far as we know – but it's a good one to begin with as it has been studied so much. It shows perception built up from simple elements, in stages, with continual feedback from higher levels that hold information about things the outside world might present to us.

123

▲Cells in the eye begin a complex process of image generation.

◀ A digital camera captures a set of pixels.

WHERE LIGHT FALLS – THE RETINA

Light passes through the lens at the front of the eye and is focused on a patch of cells at the back. We used to say that the eye stops being like a camera at that point. But perhaps the analogy works better nowadays. Modern cameras have no film, but capture the image in a photon detector that feeds electrical information to a computer processor. The eye is a little like that.

This stage of the visual system immediately shows how senses do not just receive stimuli passively. They are programmed to search. The eye is in constant motion, scanning for the important information in the visual field. Nor is the retina a passive relay. Image processing begins here.

There are two lots of photoreceptor cells right at the back of the eye. Rods sense any light, however dim. A smaller number of cones pick out details in

strong light, and respond differently to different wavelengths of light, allowing the brain to invent colours later on. Most people have three types of cones, some only two, but there are also some with four who can separate colours better than usual.

The photoreceptor cells lie beneath two other layers. Immediately above them are cells that are more or less neurons, which sense changes in the electrical potential in the photoreceptor cells and pass them on. A top layer of ganglion cells are proper neurons. They take input from the layer beneath that instructs them when to increase or decrease their rate of firing. Each ganglion cell sends a train of spikes down an axon that is routed down the optic nerve – and thus has to pass back down the layers so it can leave the back of the eye.

This slightly confusing arrangement allows the first step in processing because the ganglion cells are weighing inputs from multiple cells beneath. There are around 100 million photoreceptors, but only 1 million ganglion cells. And the intermediate layer includes "horizontal cells" that help filter the retinal input by connecting groups of cells in their own layer, and those above and below.

▼ *Microscopic anatomy of the retina.*

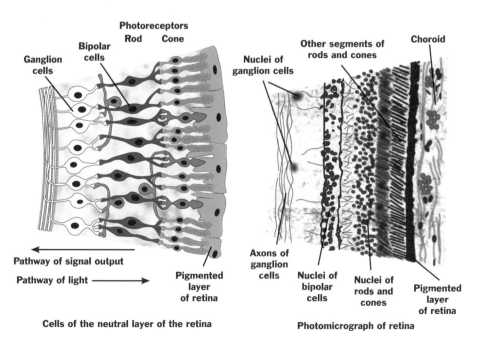

Ganglion cells

Bipolar cells

Photoreceptors
Rod   Cone

Nuclei of ganglion cells

Other segments of rods and cones

Choroid

Pathway of signal output ←

Pathway of light ⟶

Pigmented layer of retina

Axons of ganglion cells

Nuclei of bipolar cells

Nuclei of rods and cones

Pigmented layer of retina

Cells of the neutral layer of the retina

Photomicrograph of retina

SEEING THE INVISIBLE

Vision is a particularly easy sense to experiment with yourself. You can easily prove the existence of your blind spot by drawing a cross and a blob on a piece of paper about 5cm (2in) apart (see box). Cover the right eye, and stare at the blob with your left eye, move the paper closer, slowly, and you'll find a point at which the cross disappears. (Repeat for the left eye, staring at the cross until the blob disappears.)

Simple, but profound. The important thing is not that the blind spot exists, but that one is normally unaware of it. Although there's a patch of your retina, slightly off centre, with no light receptors, the brain fills in the gap.

A more elaborate blind-spot experiment convinces us that filling-

find your blind spot

BLINDSIGHT

The brain's trick of airbrushing the blind spot creates a conscious sensation in one area of the visual field with no outside input. More mysterious is a capacity shown in some people with injuries to their visual cortex. It is easiest to demonstrate when the injury only affects one hemisphere. Such patients are blind in one half of their visual field – the opposite side to the injury. But if they can be induced to guess where in that region a light flashed, without moving their eyes, they can point to the right location most of the time even though they never "saw" the flash.

▼ Seeing a flash need not be conscious – the brain can still register the light.

This ability, dubbed blindsight, extends in some cases to being able to guess whether the eyes are presented with a cross or a circle, and how a projected line is oriented. The retinal input is being received and processed in other parts of the brain, which have no access to the parts of the visual system that contribute to a conscious image. Our senses allow perception, but much of it happens below the level of awareness.

in really is happening, somehow. Project a coloured doughnut shape in front of one eye, held still. If it is placed so that the outside of the doughnut is just outside the blind spot, the inside ring just inside, the subject will see a solid coloured circle. Clear evidence, then, that the image we are conscious of is not a simple read-out, projected from the back of the retina.

WHAT CAN NEURONS "SEE"?

The best clues to how vision works have come from recordings from individual neurons in different parts of the system. That tells you something about how elements of the image in front of the eye may affect a particular cell. The response of the cell in question may be several steps on from the input but can help piece together how images are broken down by the brain.

Experiments over decades, mainly in animals, have helped establish that many different aspects of an image activate specific neurons – which allow eyes and brains to detect particular features of the scene in front of them.

As long ago as the 1930s, it was found that some cells in the much simpler visual system of a frog fire when a light is on, some when it is off, and some when the light is switched on or off. The on or off response tends to be restricted to a small part of the scene, the cell's receptive field.

The toweringly influential Hungarian-American neurophysiologist Stephen Kuffler showed in the 1950s that cells do more than seek a simple "hit" in their receptive field. Some of a frog's half a million retinal ganglion cells respond when there is light in

▶ On target: the frog's visual processing is tightly adapted to locating insect prey.

the centre of their receptive field but not the periphery. Others do the exact opposite. As often in sensory processing, the system is interested in a significant difference.

Yet more frog experiments revealed details of retinal ganglion processing. A classic 1959 paper, titled "What the frog's eye tells the frog's brain", showed how frogs fixate on small, dark, moving objects – potential insect prey – and apparently see little else. As the authors said: "The eye speaks to the brain in a language already highly interpreted, instead of transmitting a more or less accurate copy of the distribution of light on the receptors." The same is true of creatures, like us, with several more layers of processing in the visual system than the bug-hunting frog.

"SUDDENLY THE AUDIOMETER WENT OFF LIKE A MACHINE GUN"

Even with all the interpretation going on in the eye, there is a rough mapping from the retinal image to the primary visual cortex – areas close to one another in one are neighbours in the other. This is well on in visual processing, remember. But what do the cortical cells know about apart from location?

An unexpected finding in the late 1950s was illuminating. David Hubel and Torsten Wiesel were investigating cortical responses in the cat, projecting spots before a cat's eye using slides slotted into

▼ *David Hubel (left) and Torsten Wiesel in the lab.*

an ophthalmoscope. The responses were not making much sense. Then they realized that a cortical neuron they had wired with a microelectrode fired urgently when the slide dropped into the scope. As Hubel later wrote: "Suddenly the audiometer went off like a machine gun". This particular cell was responding not to a spot of light, but to a dark edge, and only when the edge was moving.

With that hint, they went on to track cells that responded to related features – lines leaning at a particular angle, or moving. The length of the line and the direction also matter.

▲ Cats have lower visual acuity than humans, and better vision in low light – but much of their cerebral processing is similar.

They also established that most of the cortical cells could register input from both eyes – unlike neurons in the visual regions of the thalamus. Signals from the two retinas have been merged somewhere along the way, although any one cell is likely to respond more strongly to one eye than the other. A radioactive labelling technique that selects for active neurons allowed them to show how this "ocular dominance" is arranged in sweeps of cells that mingle in an orderly way in this part of the cortex.

It all amounted to a deep dissection of a portion of the visual system – that won them the Nobel Prize in Physiology or Medicine in 1981. But still only a portion. The firing of these cells does not mean that a moving edge, for instance, is what is consciously seen at that moment. It is one stage in processing signals from the visual field, which then shapes input to further networks of combination and comparison higher up in the system.

ONE IMAGE, MANY MAPS

Hubel and Wiesel found cortical maps of one type of visual feature. This work has developed enormously since. Three kinds of evidence come together in piecing together visual processing. The regular standby of studying people, or animals, with brain lesions still contributes. Recording of signals from individual neurons yields more precise data. And there are studies in which specific cells are stimulated and reports from human subjects, or animals' behaviour, track the effect.

Such work reveals other areas of the cortex that register different bits and pieces of a scene. The inputs to their neurons have been set up so that they can register things like depth cues, contours, light wavelength and colour (not the same thing), and various kinds of motion. The visual cortex emerges as a mosaic of image processors, tuned to different aspects of the original input.

Researchers have followed the axon trails into areas that get to grips with further processing of all these signals from the primary visual cortex. Now the responses registered link more

directly to more complex patterns – such as a face.

We know that recognizing individual faces probably relies on a separate bit of neural analysis because there are people with normal vision who cannot do it at all. This condition of face blindness, or prosopagnosia, stops them recognizing even people they are close to, who they see every day. They report seeing a face, but cannot associate it with a particular person. They know who is who from other traits such as body size, hair or voice.

In 2005, researchers at the California Institute of Technology (Caltech) made the, well, eye-catching finding of neurons that fire when someone recognizes a particular face. The subjects were patients who accepted temporary electrode implants during treatment for epilepsy. Some had what the media gleefully dubbed "Jennifer Aniston neurons".

This is a learned response, and can be developed in a few days if a face is studied intently – happily, it works for anyone, not just faces in the media. It opens up new ways to study the changes in neural connections underlying learning and memory, not just visual recognition (see Chapter 7).

CODING A FACE

A startling finding reported in 2017 gave a glimpse of the kind of image processing the brain actually performs to register sight of a face. Doris Tsao's team at Caltech studied small sets of cells in macaque brains already identified as "face patches".

They were able to get deep into the coding happening in these patches, revealing: "a remarkably simple code for facial identity... that can be used to both precisely decode realistic face images from population responses and accurately predict neural firing rates".

▶ Realistic image rendering by computer requires heavy-duty data processing. Perhaps our brains are more subtle?

◀ We can recognize a face from surprisingly few inputs – but how?

What this means is they found that individual neurons responded, not to a particular face, but to simple characteristics of faces.

Their experiment began with an abstract coding system for breaking down images of faces into a set of 50 simple measurements. They used this code to create 200 different computer-generated faces which differed in precisely measured ways.

Exposing monkeys to these images, they found that individual neurons in face patches respond to particular facial measurements. Once they had mapped enough cells, they were able to reconstruct the human faces monkeys were looking at from the neuronal response. The match between the original and inferred images was so good they suggested that the brain itself must be using their code.

If so, they have a close match to the actual working of a key perceptual ability. It suggests that a couple of hundred neurons in a primate are encoding details of faces. Each one fixates on one axis in the space of all possible faces. If a set of faces look wildly different, but all measure the same in the dimension a neuron is sensitized to, it will respond the same way to each of them. The whole ensemble of neurons is needed to discriminate between faces.

Recognizing a familiar face will still involve other brain areas, but this is a powerful new insight into the original coding. Even a much-loved face is first reduced to geometry. Researchers speculate that future work will show how shapes of other complicated objects are encoded in similar, relatively simple ways.

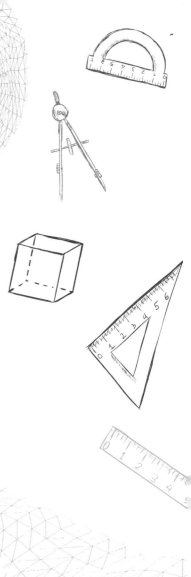

PICTURE THE SCENE

The broad outline of the visual system has been traced fairly well. Processing begins at the back of the eye, and continues in the thalamus and the various regions of the visual cortex. There is much overlap, and much redundancy in this, as in other sensory systems. But the results of all these analyses then pass mainly to the parietal lobe – a pathway known as the dorsal route – or to the temporal and frontal lobes via the ventral route.

They were originally dubbed the "where" and "what" pathways, with the idea that one specializes in spatial information, while the other handles more sophisticated business-like identification. In fact, both pathways are involved in decoding what and where. But the dorsal path does appear to produce outputs related to action, while the ventral path leads on to areas more concerned with recognition.

The whole set-up raises a variation on a classic question. We often ask when it makes sense to treat the brain as a set of separate modules, and when to consider it operating as a whole.

Similarly, study of the visual system suggests that our brain is a bit of a reductionist. It breaks down an image into many different components: a moving spot of light here, an edge there, an aperture, a contour, a contrast between two colours, a pattern that resembles a face, and so on.

And yet... while someone with normal vision can pick out any of those things on demand, we normally experience a scene as undivided. It isn't at all clear how that feeling is created. Francis Crick, prospecting the future of neuroscience 30 years ago, reckoned that we know a lot about how the brain takes an image apart, but not how it puts it back together. That is still a fair summary.

That overlooks another question, though. Does the brain need some

▲ *Abstract artists can suggest features of a scene with a few strokes – if our brains supply the missing detail.*

special region of neural network where the image is assembled? But that quickly turns into a much harder question. Can we identify the seat of consciousness? We'll come back to that, but there won't be a simple answer there, either.

what can you see, dog or cats?

GOOD VIBES

Stand back from the detail, and two things stand out about the visual system. The inputs are processed in different ways through several stages. And there are rich, heavily used connections up and down the levels, helping the brain generate and test hypotheses about what's out there.

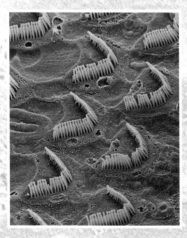

▲ The organ of Corti, part of the cochlea where hair cells turn vibrations into axon spikes.

▼ Hair cells in the inner ear.

The details aren't so well understood, but those features can be found in the way the brain handles sound, too. The sensory cells this time turn vibrations, transmitted from the air outside to fluid inside the spiralling cochlea in the inner ear, into axon spikes. The cells, known as hair cells, are extraordinarily sensitive. They have tiny cilia that can generate a response when they move as little as 0.3nm (nanometers), about the width of an atom.

The signals generated pass to a nerve relay, and thence into the brainstem. There is a whole set of pathways they can follow from there to the first part of the cortex involved in analysing sound, yet to be fully traced. We do know that the cochlear membrane that supports hair cells is engineered so that it responds to different frequencies along its length, and the cells' relative positions are preserved in the first cortical mapping.

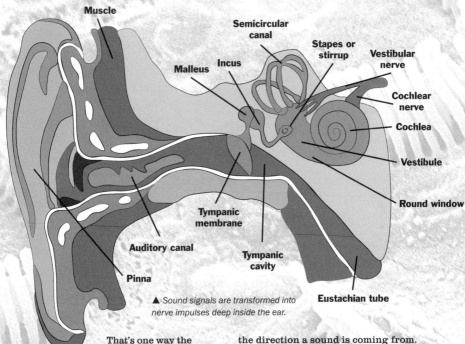

▲ Sound signals are transformed into nerve impulses deep inside the ear.

Labels:
Muscle
Semicircular canal
Stapes or stirrup
Vestibular nerve
Malleus
Incus
Cochlear nerve
Cochlea
Vestibule
Round window
Tympanic membrane
Auditory canal
Tympanic cavity
Pinna
Eustachian tube

That's one way the system keeps track of frequencies. Another takes advantage of the fact that the stimulus in this system – audible sound – is at frequencies in the range of neuron firing. That means that frequencies up to about 5,000 hertz (from the human audible range of 20–20,000) can also be registered by neurons that generate axon spikes at the same rate.

Hearing also has to register intensity, and subtle differences in intensity and timing allow analysis of the direction a sound is coming from.

The more complex processing that ensues involves neurons that respond to similar tones, to complex mixtures of frequencies, or sounds that rise or fall in frequency (think of a blues guitar player bending a string), and some that register differences in duration.

Then there is the symbolic side of sound, which relies on yet more processing via connections with areas involved with language, like the one Broca identified, long ago.

SOMETHING IN THE AIR

> *"Smells are surer than sounds or sights to make your heartstrings crack."*

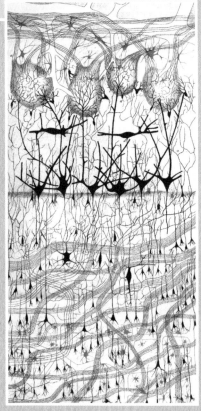

▼ This drawing of neurons in the olfactory bulb of a dog was made by Golgi in 1875.

Look at a dog walking unrestrained down a city street. It is constantly in motion, its snout diving from one spot to another, scanning for new scent. It's a reminder that each creature uses its senses to search out valuable information, not as passive receivers of signals.

We notice this in the dog because it dwells near the ground, and has invested heavily in reading smells. The canine olfactory epithelium – the layer of cells at the back of the nasal cavity where smell begins – can have 200 million receptor cells. We upright bipeds, who prioritize vision, make do with 5 million.

Still, scent is powerful. "Smells are surer than sounds or sights to make your heartstrings crack," wrote Kipling. Neuroscience backs this up. Molecules wafted to the back of the nose activate cells that pass information along cranial nerve fibres via the olfactory bulb and the thalamus directly to the hippocampus and amygdala, brain regions that rouse emotion.

Strictly, we are detecting odours in water, not air, as scent molecules are dissolved in mucus before they can bind with their receptors. Molecular detectors first evolved in a watery medium, and have operated in it ever since.

The importance of smell is shown again by the diversity of receptors. The mammalian gene family of olfactory receptors was discovered in the 1990s, and runs to 1,000 different genes in rodents. Humans have dispensed with many but still have at least 350 different receptors. Most olfactory cells only make one kind of receptor, and signals from each kind of receptor are directed to the same region of the olfactory bulb.

Once again, the system features overlap and redundancy. Each receptor recognizes a number of different molecules, and any given molecule can activate different receptors, to a varying extent. Almost everyone thinks receptors are responding to molecular shape, though there are alternative theories to account for the diversity of smell response that delve into quantum mechanics.

Higher level processing then analyses the pattern of signals from a particular molecular mix to generate the sensation of a particular odour. We know we can discriminate many thousands of smells, and the upper limit is probably much higher than that.

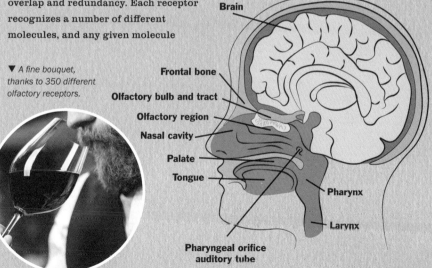

▼ A fine bouquet, thanks to 350 different olfactory receptors.

Brain

Frontal bone

Olfactory bulb and tract

Olfactory region

Nasal cavity

Palate

Tongue

Pharynx

Larynx

Pharyngeal orifice auditory tube

TASTY

Taste is the second chemical sense, and a bit simpler than smell. That makes sense if you think of smell as a first line of defence against dangerous chemicals. Smell is always there first. You can decline to look, listen, touch or taste, but interrupting smell requires you to stop breathing. Taste will tell you to spit out some noxious mouthfuls, but it seems mainly adapted to reinforcing preferences rather than prompting avoidance.

sweet

bitter

sour

salty

umami

The relatively coarse discrimination of the system starts at the receptor end, with 5,000–10,000 human taste buds on the tongue and other parts of the mouth, each with perhaps 100 sensory cells.

The five basic tastes – sweet, salty, bitter, sour and the recent addition umami, or savoury – rely on neural signals created by receptors that work in different ways. Saltiness and sourness depend on special channel proteins, for sodium ions and hydrogen ions, respectively. The other tastes come from a family of shape-based receptors, with bitterness the largest receptor class, perhaps reflecting the range of toxic chemicals different plants manufacture that are best avoided. All these details come from 21st-century research, and the precise ways receptor signals are resolved into tastes remain elusive. We do know, though, that smell receptors, interacting with molecules from chewed food, contribute strongly to overall flavour sensation.

the five tastes

TASTE CELLS

You can see the small bumps – papillae – on your tongue where taste buds wait to sense incoming chemicals. But in the last couple of decades, cell mappers have identified the same detectors in other parts of the body. We aren't consciously aware of these as they are not connected to the brain region that processes signals from taste buds. Bitter taste receptors in the intestine probably help produce involuntary reactions to spoiled food. Similar cells in the nose and lungs help induce sneezing when they sense products of harmful bacteria.

Sweetness receptors in the intestine appear not to connect directly with the nervous system, but affect hormone release that aids digestion. There are yet more taste cells, such as those in the bile duct, whose functions remain speculative.

▼ Papillae on the surface of the tongue.

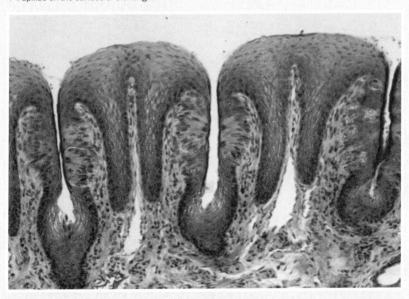

TOUCHY-FEELY

Touch, like smell, is obviously functional but also powerfully emotional. Talking about our feelings about someone, or of being touched, is both metaphorical and not.

Skin is our largest sense organ. It senses texture, vibration and pressure, as well as heat, cold and pain. It can produce near-instant responses to external events, such as treading on glass. But it also joins the search for information associated with other senses. Think of identifying the right coin for a slot machine by feeling in your pocket. Your fingers have to move to register the shapes and sizes you encounter.

In more complex creatures, the simple physical encounter with objects is still important. But touch also takes on fundamental roles in communication – grooming, cuddles, caresses and kisses, even tickling, are woven into our social, sexual and family lives.

◀ *Skin to skin touch communicates powerfully.*

TOUCH CELLS

All this begins with an array of different receptors. "Touch cells" identified by German anatomist Friedrich Merkel back in the 1870s are now known as Merkel cells, and a small set of them in a Merkel disc responds to edges and rough textured surfaces. They fire as long as a touch stimulus lasts, as do the scattered nerve endings known as Ruffini endings, which sense skin stretching and hence pressure. The basic quartet of touch sensors is completed by two types of cells, one near the skin surface, one deeper, that mainly register low-frequency and high-frequency vibrations, respectively.

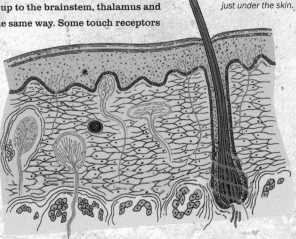

▲ A Merkel cell.

As well as these force-sensing receptors, the skin also has free nerve endings that confer other sensitivities. They register light touches, and they are the points of origin for compelling sensations including pain, chemical stings, inflammation, and itching, as well as heat and cold. There are additional nerve endings in hairy skin (the majority, when you look up close) that sense hair movement.

All these receptors and nerve fibres feed signals into the spinal cord and thence up to the brainstem, thalamus and cortex. But not all in the same way. Some touch receptors are linked by fast fibres, and convey signals that allow good resolution in time and space. Others, found only in hairy skin, have slower connections, and respond to, for example, someone stroking your arm.

▼ Different types of touch receptors lie just under the skin.

A DELICATE PROBING

Surgical treatment for epilepsy hasn't just yielded insights for neuroscience by separating hemispheres. The Canadian Wilder Penfield explored the surface of the cerebral cortex, especially the strip that handles touch receptor signals, by gently probing the brain with electrodes prior to surgery, and asking conscious patients what they felt. The immediate aim was to take out small pieces of cortex producing seizures without damaging normal tissue, but following work with 400 patients he built up a bigger picture.

He began the work in the 1930s and much of it has stood up to testing by other methods – with many detailed refinements. It also produced some of the most famous images in neuroscience.

In 1950, he co-authored a paper with an illustration by medical artist Hortense Cantlie which showed different regions of the body as they mapped both the sensory and motor strips of the cortex. The size of each part of the image matched the portion of cortex in which it was represented, with the lips, tongue, and hands and feet all greatly enlarged.

The same data was used to reassemble a human-shaped model, with similar expansions, and the sensory homunculus became a famous exhibit in London's Natural History Museum. It may have given the impression there was a tiny, distorted figure somewhere in the head, but it was still a popular gateway to neuroscience.

Neither Penfield nor Cantlie made an equivalent image for females – a hermunculus? The surgeon treated fewer female patients, and may also have been inhibited in reporting, or even inquiring, about genital sensation in women. That sensory mapping for women is still not fully detailed.

In fact, Penfield erred in his mapping of the male genitalia too. He located their (somewhat enlarged) sensory inputs adjacent to the cortical area that connects to the feet, and suggested this might be at the root of foot fetishes. However, more recent findings locate the penis in a more familiar position relative to other cortical areas.

REACH OUT AND I'LL BE THERE

Almost everyone craves sexual contact, but interpersonal touch has plenty of less obvious roles in relationships. Rodents groom and lick their pups and humans cuddle their babies. Deprivation on either score causes distressing developmental problems.

▲ Premature babies feel the benefit of the gentlest touching.

The extreme evidence here comes from children in orphanages with too few staff, and premature babies who have to be kept alive in incubators. Immediate effects include slower growth, weakened immune systems and poor cognitive development. Children who spent their infancy in Romanian orphanages before the country's change of regime in 1989 grew into teenagers with less white matter than normal in their brains.

A range of diseases, and psychiatric disorders, are more likely in later life, too.

On the other hand, controlled studies show benefits from relatively short bouts of touching, 15–20 minutes, for both children and adults. It can be done impersonally, by massage, but other research shows that we are pretty good at reading emotion from a gesture as simple as a touch on the arm. The connections here between skin surface and brain are subtle and deep. Still, there is plenty of variation between cultures in how we use them. A simple observational study in the 1960s recorded that couples in cafés touched each other 100 times an hour on average. That was in Puerto Rico. The average in London back then? Zero.

RATS ENJOY BEING TICKLED TOO

You can include the mechanism of tickling in the list of intriguing unsolved problems of neuroscience. But there are new avenues opening up for researchers. A few years ago, researchers discovered that lab rats can be lightly tickled – and will seek out the lab-worker's hand for a repeat. They even emit the rat equivalent of a giggle, an ultrasonic squeak. And the origin of the response appears to be linked to the somatosensory cortex, contrary to earlier theorizing which envisaged activity in the emotional centres of the brain. Rats that are used to playful tickling show increased neuronal activity in their somatosensory regions during and *after* tickling, and stimulating the cells concerned electrically can elicit the same pleasure-signalling squeaks as the original tickling.

CROSSED WIRES?

The idea that what happens in the brain contributes at least as much to our sense of the world as signals from sensory neurons is reinforced by our ability to conjure up entire non-existent events, in dreams and hallucinations.

But there's an intermediate case that also sheds light on how perception works. Some people experience a perception of something others confirm is "really" there – one of the letters on this page, say – combined with a quality that is not. They might see the letter y of "say" as red instead of black.

Perceiving letters or musical tones as colours is one of the more common variants, but almost any blend seems possible, with taste and smell coming into the mix as well.

Theories of synaesthesia focus on unusual cross wirings between brain regions – the letter-processing and colour-generating areas of the visual cortex, for example. Some researchers suspect babies begin as synaesthetes, and most learn to separate sensory channels. The incidence of some kind of synaesthesia in adults isn't known, but

one careful survey suggested it may be around 4 per cent, in both men and women.

The enhanced sensory experience synaesthesia offers has inspired artists and poets. The multilingual writer Vladimir Nabokov detailed his richly decorated experience of the world, with distinct colours for letters in more than one alphabet. "The confessions of a synesthete must sound tedious to those who are protected from such leaking and drafts by more solid walls than mine are," he wrote.

NICE TRY, BRAIN

Some perceptions classified as synaesthesia seem closer kin to hallucinations. University of California neuroscientist V S Ramachandran reports a case of a man who went blind as an adult and learned to read Braille. This implies a major change in connections within the brain, as touch signals adapt to more intensive use. A few years later, he began to see flashes of light, or stark images when he touched an object, or read Braille. He had no control over whether this happened, and found they got in the way of what he was trying to understand through touch. Ramachandran speculates that his somatosensory cortex is sending signals to "his deprived visual areas, which are hungry for input".

▲ Learning to read braille rewires parts of the cerebral cortex, but not always helpfully.

MAKING SENSE

There is still much to learn about each of the five senses examined briefly here. The same is true of the sixth, proprioception, which allows us to keep track of our body in space and what forces act on it. The basic details though are similar. Cellular sensors that register pressure, force and movement generate nerve signals that are integrated, seemingly automatically. The signals this time come from inside the body, but still from outside the brain, which uses them to infer the state of, in this case, its most immediate surroundings.

That notion, of inference, along with active search, is probably the most important idea from study of the senses. We don't always know how it works but it is happening. The senses don't simply give read-outs, like dials on a

◀ A lot to make sense of. This man's brain can turn this vast array of visual stimuli into a cityscape – a thing that only humans can understand.

dashboard. They provide raw data for computational (we assume) modelling of our surroundings.

David Linden of Johns Hopkins University summarizes this view in his book *Touch*. "Our touch circuits", he writes, "are not built to be faithful reporters of the outside world but are constructed to make inferences about the tactile world based on expectations – expectations derived from both the historical experiences of our human ancestors and from our own individual experiences."

And so it is for all the senses, which evolved to allow the brain to build a model of the external world as an aid to survival. This fits the evidence about how neuronal networks transform the inputs from sensory nerves. It is also a validation of much earlier suggestions about the mechanisms of the senses. Hermann Helmholtz, summarizing his own studies of vision in the 1860s, proposed that "none of our sensations give us anything more than 'signs' for external objects and movements, and...we can only learn how to *interpret* these signs by means of experience and practice."

It is a difficult conclusion to hold on to, though. Almost all the brain work here is unconscious, and our conscious experience of our perceptions allowing us to navigate the real world apparently effortlessly is compelling. And that is reinforced when we use our perceptions to guide what the system is really all about – action.

▼ *Clever computer rendering turns a technical drawing into a photo-realistic image of a building – another example of building a scene from limited input.*

CHAPTER 6

MOTION AND EMOTION

ANCIENT AND MODERN

Much of the human brain, like any other, is tied up with basic functions. Many are automated hormonal or neuronal loops that keep the body's systems operating smoothly. Then there are the systems that control movement – very likely one of the reasons brains were needed in the first place. All action calls on movement. Emotions, at root, are concerned with regulating actions. Both arise in neural circuits that, in humans, first appeared in regions of ancient origin but now link almost all parts of the brain.

The basics of motion can be studied in isolated nerve and muscle preparations, and are pretty well understood. Just as the senses depend on specialized cells that link events outside the body with neurons, so muscle contraction depends on particular motor neurons that synapse directly with muscle cells.

Some reflex actions arise from circuits in the spinal cord, but more complex motion calls for commands from the brain. Either way, the final result is activation of an axonal signal from a motor neuron. It meets a muscle cell at the neuromuscular junction, where it releases the neurotransmitter acetylcholine. This triggers electrical changes in the muscle cell that make a muscle fibre twitch – one action potential from the axon produces one twitch.

The detailed wiring varies, with slow and fast muscle fibres connected to subtly different motor neurons. The force a muscle exerts is controlled by variations

◄ *Motor neurons in muscle tissue.*

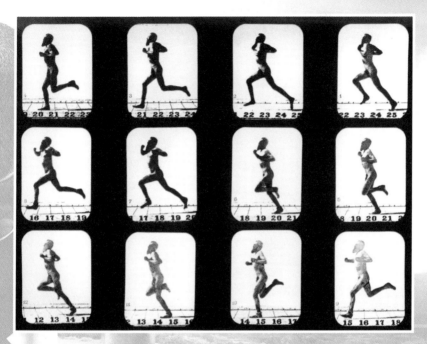

▲ *Human motion captured by pioneer photographer Edward Muybridge in 1881.*

in the rate of firing and by the number of fibres. In the leg, one neuron can activate more than 1,000 muscle fibres, while small muscles moving eyes or fingers may have only a few fibres connected to each motor neuron. Most muscles have a range of motor neurons, some recruiting lots of fibres, some a smaller number, to help produce graduated movements.

Each motor neuron has one output channel, as normal, and receives inputs from three main routes. The largest number of connections are from other neurons in the spinal cord. There are inputs from the brain, as you'd expect. Finally, there are inputs from sensors in the muscle itself, connected via the spine, that monitor how much it has contracted.

CONTROLLED MOVEMENT

Motor neurons and muscle fibres have to produce movements of all kinds, from a weightlifter's heave to the smallest adjustment of a calligrapher's brush. Either way, the main commands for voluntary movements begin in the frontal lobes of the cerebral cortex. The strip known as the motor cortex lies just in front of the sensory cortex, and is mapped to body parts in much the same way. The motor homunculus thus looks similar to the sensory homunculus (see page 146).

Much of it is devoted to the fingers, so let's focus on them. The motor cortex has different areas for simple movements, like finger waggling, and for finer digital dexterity. For the latter, the supplementary motor cortex passes inputs to the primary motor cortex before they are sent on to the muscles, helping orchestrate complex sequences.

The motor cortex also relays its signals to the cerebellum, which coordinates muscle pairs (muscles can only contract, and work in opposed pairs) and organizes the timing of movements, and to the parietal lobes of the cortex. Several other brain regions are involved in evaluating and modulating movements, too.

Motion can be finely adjusted because of the intricate connections in the remote cells that make the actual movement.

The thumb, for instance, has more than ten different muscles. The thousands of muscle fibres making up each of them all respond to commands from a single motor neuron, selected from multiple original connections during early development.

That's just the thumb. Most often its movement will also have to be coordinated with the other fingers, each with their own muscles, and with the movement of the hand, arm and rest of the body, all while staying balanced and perhaps tracking an object the hand is reaching for. Computer programmers still struggle to engineer robots that can pick up, say, a cup full of water without dropping or spilling it.

That said, fine movements are fascinating, but our motor system is also well adapted to what it does more of the time, holding still.

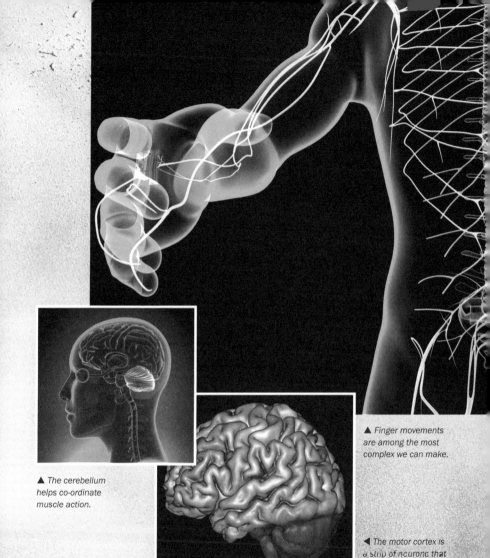

▲ Finger movements
are among the most
complex we can make.

▲ The cerebellum
helps co-ordinate
muscle action.

◄ The motor cortex is
a strip of neurons that
lies next to the main
sensory cortex.

MOTION RELIES ON SENSATION

Building robots shows how hard it is to control motion. Work on prosthetic limbs also yields insight into how control in our own system relies on sensory feedback.

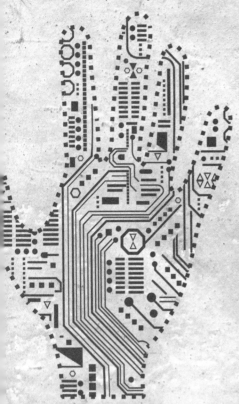

Some artificial limbs now respond to signals from the motor cortex that are decoded to disclose intentions for moving a new arm or hand. It's a remarkable technical feat, allowing a user to move the limb by thought alone.

But it turns out that is only half the job. Fine control of the hand normally depends on feedback from touch sensors. An artificial hand without such cues forces the user to rely on visual feedback, which does not work nearly as well.

Sliman Bensmaia of the University of Chicago and his collaborators are looking for ways of sending touch sensations to the sensory cortex that could one day match movements, essentially reproducing normal proprioception for an artificial limb.

At the moment, the work focuses on monkeys, who cannot report their sensations directly but can be trained to indicate where they feel a touch. Experiments intersperse real touches with signals sent artificially to the sensory

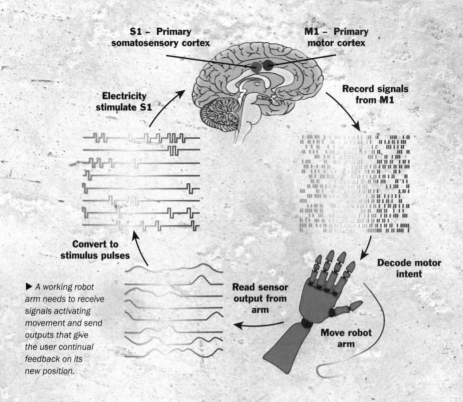

S1 – Primary somatosensory cortex

M1 – Primary motor cortex

Electricity stimulate S1

Record signals from M1

Convert to stimulus pulses

Decode motor intent

▶ *A working robot arm needs to receive signals activating movement and send outputs that give the user continual feedback on its new position.*

Read sensor output from arm

Move robot arm

cortex to confirm the mapping decoded by earlier experimenters.

The future vision, still some way off, is for a prosthetic hand with sensors that send signals to the right places in the sensory cortex to indicate when each part of the hand touches something, and improve guidance for the next move.

This assumes that the sensation is "felt" in the artificial hand, not the native hand. Although people who lose a limb often report continued sensations in a phantom extremity, there is evidence that the brain can adjust to the presence of a prosthetic limb, and allow sensation to shift to the new addition.

STROLLING ALONG

If you hold up a new baby and let its feet touch the ground, it will begin to step, like an adult walking on the spot. But the baby won't be able to walk unaided for many months. The action we rely on to get us about the place has many components, only some of which are ready to use at birth.

The basic step is driven by a simple locomotor pattern that arises in the spinal cord. Animals can do it when the connection to the brain is severed. It relies on ancient circuitry that appears first in fish. In us, it generates a rhythmic movement that doesn't need any conscious input. The computer analogy for neural circuitry should be treated with caution, but it does look like a simple program that takes care of a basic routine. Breathing is controlled in much the same way.

Mastering the use of this rhythm to actually walk is harder for us than other creatures because we only use two legs – turning walking into a kind of controlled falling. The simplest rhythmic walk, such as on a treadmill, still calls on the brain to integrate information from the vestibular system – sensory neurons in ear canals that register gravitational forces – the eyes, and pressure sensors on the soles of the feet. All help adjust the upper body and the swinging arms so that the walker's centre of gravity stays more or less above the feet.

If nothing changes, it's easy to maintain a steady gait, but speed up the treadmill, or make it slope up or down, and there's a hefty load of instant processing to do to adjust skeletal

muscles. It is still largely unconscious, though increasing the demand – on uneven ground, or the deck of a ship in a heavy swell, say – can change that. But think about where you are placing your feet, and you slow down. Best to let the mature motion system take care of it. Then you'll only be conscious of how much you rely on it when it goes awry, as when you misjudge the last step in a flight of stairs.

▶ Don't overthink it: climbing stairs automatically is faster than pondering where to place your feet.

WHY PRACTICE MAKES PERFECT

▲ Very slick, but you didn't see them before they practised the routine.

Fine control requires dedicated neurons, and more get involved when someone works on new skills. Practising movements helps strengthen neural connections that allow you to learn a routine (see Chapter 7) but may involve more extensive changes in neural connections.

There is a notable plasticity in the motor cortex, which helps. Some people are born with two or three fingers fused together – a condition known as syndactyly. Their motor cortex map develops so that the joined fingers are represented by a single set of neurons.

If the digits are separated surgically later on, the cortical map reorganizes to suit, with new areas that differentiate between the freed fingers.

There are also numerous studies that track changes in brain scans while musicians hone their skills. Violinists, for example, develop larger motor cortex areas for their left hand, which does all the fancy fingering, than for the right, which controls the bow. Other evidence indicates that professional musicians have more synapses in the motor cortex than matched non-musicians.

What about trying to learn an instrument if you have no musical training? A team at McGill University in Montreal investigated this with a group of beginning piano players in their 20s or 30s in 2015. Fifteen men and women tried to learn to play a selection of familiar pop songs, nursery rhymes and carols, practising for half an hour a day for five weeks.

You cannot play a keyboard inside a scanner, yet, so they made before and after functional magnetic resonance imaging (fMRI) scans while listening to, but not playing, music.

The scans showed changes in the premotor cortex and parietal cortex as people's learning developed. But practice isn't everything, and those with scans suggesting more activity at the outset in the auditory cortex and the hippocampus, in areas the researchers inferred are involved in dissecting and memorizing melodies, learned faster.

The authors of this study suggest that most complex skills involve more than muscle memory. So practising movement will get results, but some people will start with advantages because of differences in other parts of their brains.

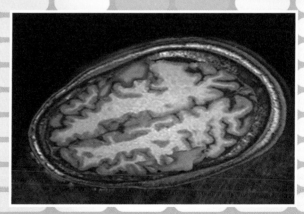

▶ MRI can track brain activity while a subject listens to music.

I HAVE FEELINGS

Fear, anger, sadness, jealousy, love, happiness, surprise, disgust. The urgency of our emotions suggests they matter. We can have idle thoughts, but not idle emotions. Yet it is hard to define emotions, or – a distinction some researchers make – their conscious manifestation as feelings. They are not quite like perceptions, although emotions are cued by sensory inputs and part of emotion, we assume, is some kind of representation of them. Nor are they actions, though they may provoke action. But they are definitely telling us that something important is going on.

Emotions have some qualities in common, but they aren't all alike. And it has proved difficult to pin down brain areas that are involved. Some regions, often tiny ones, are essential for particular emotions. But many parts of the brain are involved in all of them. It is possible to outline sensory systems, like the visual system, in detail, although they do seem to

become more ramified as research moves on. But efforts to define an emotional system have been largely superseded by findings about the breadth of the networks involved.

It is still useful to have a quick rundown of the areas that are definitely involved in emotion. They are still often referred to as the "limbic system", shorthand for a collection of parts of the brain that lie close together beneath the cortex. They include:

* the thalamus
* the hypothalamus
* the amygdala
* the hippocampus

The latter's involvement in emotion appears less important than its contributions to memory.

All are connected to each other and to the rest of the brain in overlapping networks, and each, although small, has more even smaller anatomically distinct areas, or nuclei.

There's plenty of research on the specifics of their involvement in particular emotions. And we know that emotions are tied in to powerful physiological reactions, often stoked up by hormones made in the brain. One emotion stands out as perhaps the best understood in this work – fear, and its focus in the amygdala.

A FEAR CIRCUIT?

The amygdala, the almond-shaped region, has numerous distinguishable nuclei, but it gets input via two main routes. One comes from the thalamus, which samples the senses, and sends on selected urgent signals. The other comes down from part of the prefrontal cortex. Both are involved in the responses that produce fear and anxiety.

▲ Hardwired? People fear snakes, even if they have never seen one before.

Some fears, like shying away from snakes, are instinctive. These disappear when the amygdala is damaged. More elaborate experiments have shown that it is also active when we acquire new fears based on our experience of bad things happening – fear conditioning.

The opposite process, gradually losing a fear response when the feared stimulus repeats without the pain – physical or mental – has also been investigated. It depends on a neurotransmitter receptor known as the NMDA receptor, which plays a key role in one of the best understood facets of synaptic change linked to learning – to be discussed in the next chapter.

The fear response here does not necessarily mean the feeling of being afraid. Animals show the same physiological responses as we do, but we have no idea about their feelings. The amygdala is concerned with the things we do share with them when there is danger – which it encourages with a battery of neurotransmitters and hormones.

Other findings that dovetail with these include a role for at least some parts of the amygdala in recognizing fearful expressions in other people, and work on neurotransmitter levels in this region, especially serotonin and dopamine.

This ought not to mean that we label the amygdala the brain's fear centre, cautions Joseph LeDoux, one of the leaders in this research. It certainly helps detect threats, and trigger the classic "fight or flight" response. And the direct input from the thalamus means the response begins before any conscious awareness of the threat.

But the actual feeling of fear can arise without the amygdala. It arises from a more complex evaluation of the whole system by parts of the cortex. Neuroscience begins with words like fear, that have everyday meanings, says LeDoux, but we must avoid treating the words "as if they are entities that live in brain areas, like the amygdala".

▶ *Janet Leigh's character in Alfred Hitchcock's Psycho discovers a reason to be fearful.*

EMOTION, MIND AND BODY

Emotion is often seen as a driver of action, but one that should be kept separate from decision. This fits the idea that the limbic system is a primitive part of the brain that is tamed by the more sophisticated apparatus of the cortex. It is an echo of the triune brain notion that was influential in the 1950s (see Small Steps, page 72). The same researcher, Paul MacLean, who popularized the triune brain thesis also introduced the term limbic system.

Recently, though, the more or less opposite view has come to seem more plausible. Antonio Damasio of the University of Southern California argues that emotion is the result of actions, albeit internal ones. Perceiving a physical threat – a wolf coming your way – triggers

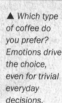

▲ Which type of coffee do you prefer? Emotions drive the choice, even for trivial everyday decisions.

◀ Antonio Damasio.

changes in the body. The heart races. Adrenaline rises. Blood is diverted from the stomach to the muscles. The cortex then reads these automatic responses as fear, which is a blend of responses from brain and body. Another way to put it is that the five senses create representations of external states in the brain, but the emotions are representations of body states.

Damasio also finds emotion strongly linked to the other kind of action. People with brain damage that, one way or another, makes them lose touch with their emotions tend to make terrible decisions. Their general intelligence and language abilities are more or less normal. But they have little idea how to weigh risks and benefits, are poor planners, and share embarrassing information freely. Worse, lacking identifiable appetites or desires, they may become unable to make any decisions at all. The notion of ideal decisions as a matter of coolly detached, rational appraisal may appeal in the abstract, but bears no resemblance to what our brains evolved to achieve.

It is a big shift in neuroscience's outlook. Damasio declares that, when he started research on emotion in the 1970s, he was told, "Well, you're going to be lost, because there's absolutely nothing there of consequence." Now he feels able to assert that feelings are "mental experiences of body states".

So hunger, for example, arises from physiological need, pain from injury, fear and anger from threats to the organism. On the positive side, wellbeing is a sign of optimal functioning. And compassion, gratitude, even love, are ways of regulating "specific social interactions". Emotions, in short, are woven into every aspect of life, by both body and mind. In fact, he goes further: "Mind begins at the level of feeling. It's when you have a feeling (even if you're a very little creature) that you begin to have a mind and a self."

As with Helmholtz's approach to the senses, this is in some ways a recovery of an insight aired back in the 19th century. William James, Harvard's first professor of psychology, wrote in his essay "What is an Emotion?" in 1884 that: "If we fancy some strong emotion, and then try to abstract from our consciousness of it all the feelings of its characteristic bodily symptoms, we find we have nothing left behind, no 'mind stuff' out of which the emotion can be constituted, and that a cold and neutral state of intellectual perception is all that remains."

▲ Adrenaline, crystallized.
◄ William James.

EMOTION DISABLED

Elliot, a man in his 30s studied by Antonio Damasio, had a large brain tumour removed, along with much of his frontal lobe. After surgery, he was intellectually intact, save for applying himself to decisions. Lacking all emotion, he found it impossible to schedule appointments, decide where to go for lunch, even choose a colour to write with. His marriage fell apart and he lost his job. He married again, divorced again, and started several ill-advised business ventures, which left him bankrupt.

He seemed not to mind much. When he described his life, writes Damasio, "Nowhere was there a sense of his own suffering, even though he was the protagonist." He had no strong feelings about all his setbacks. And when tested on the options he could envisage for dealing with a range of situations, he readily outlined a set of normal, sensible outcomes, then said, calmly, "And after all this, I still wouldn't know what to do!"

MIRROR, MIRROR

When someone says "I feel your pain", can it be literally true? Well, empathy is recognized as an admirable human trait. And a special class of neurons may help us feel others' emotions.

Mirror neurons were first identified in studies of movement. In the 1990s, researchers in Italy reported that some cells in a monkey's premotor cortex would fire when they made a movement, and when they saw another monkey move the same way.

Moreover, some of the motor-network neurons responded to certain movements when the monkey simply heard another perform an action – such as crinkling up a sheet of paper. This could suggest that the listeners were decoding the intention behind an action as opposed to just rehearsing it in their own brains.

This is not evidence for empathy, but was widely interpreted as a way in which one brain can understand more readily what another brain is trying to do. MRI studies suggest that similar neurons probably exist in human brains, too, and they have been granted a whole range of powers, from conferring actual empathy to promoting imitation and accelerating the development of human culture.

The notion that empathy involves some kind of repeat of an emotion in the observer's brain has some support from general MRI studies that show increased activity in the same brain regions when someone experiences an emotion and when they see someone else getting emotional. But this is not evidence for involvement of mirror neurons, if indeed they exist in the emotion-regulating areas of the brain.

Mirror neurons quickly became a fashionable research area, but there were as many publications critical of the large claims made for their significance as supporting them.

The objections are many and varied, but one of the more persuasive ones is that just because seeing (or hearing) something triggers a response in a neuron that is involved if the viewer performs the same action does not necessarily mean that the neuron in question is involved in understanding the action. It could be a learned association that has some quite different use in the brain.

The same would apply to mirror neurons active in emotional states. For now, it seems best to conclude that, while empathy must have some underlying neural mechanism, teasing it out awaits further research.

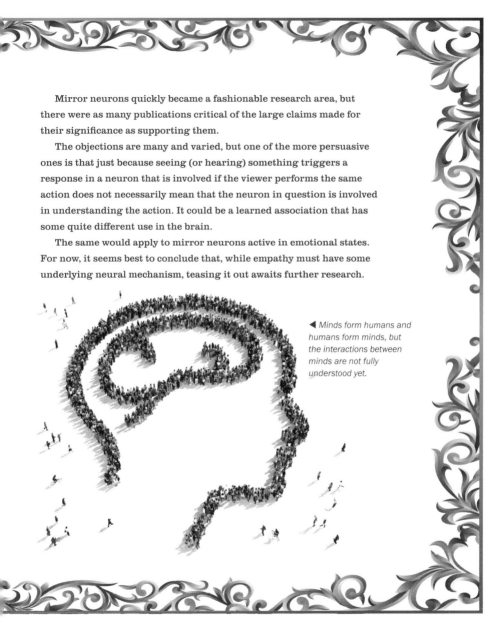

◀ *Minds form humans and humans form minds, but the interactions between minds are not fully understood yet.*

LOVE IS BLIND

We know something of how the rewards of love are registered in the brain – through centres that register the effects of the neurotransmitter dopamine and the hormone oxytocin, among other signalling chemicals. And in line with their importance in our lives, the feelings and emotions associated with love involve many different regions of the brain.

It is easy to imagine why they evolved – to promote reproduction and successful child-rearing. Most of the work aimed at deepening neuroscientific insights into love has relied on fMRI, so has the normal limitations of a relatively coarse scan and indirect inferences about which brain regions are active.

How to study love? Well, it was Helen's face that launched a thousand ships, so perhaps start with faces. And a study at the turn of the millennium did show differences in brain scans when people looked at photos of a lover or someone who was just a friend. A small number of areas were more active on seeing a lover – three in the cerebral cortex and several others in subcortical areas. Is it surprising that so few areas show up in this comparison? The researchers point out that they are, as usual, connected to lots of other sites.

Such studies show the expected activity in the systems involved in reward (discussed in Chapter 9). And there are hints about some of the other aspects of love. Pathways

that have been linked to negative emotions, and negative assessment of others, are relatively less active in people who say they are in love – confirming the widespread, if unromantic, perception that love dulls the critical faculties. Semir Zeki of University College London suggests that "we are often surprised by the choice of partner someone makes, asking futilely whether they have taken leave of their senses. In fact, they have. Love is often irrational because rational judgments are suspended."

Attachment is a crucial aspect of romantic and parental love, but there is evidence that they involve different cortical networks. Maternal love is associated with increased activation in regions involved in face recognition but does not show activation of regions of the hypothalamus that respond to both sexual arousal and romantic love. The suppression of negative judgements may be common to both, however.

MY COMPANY IS LIKE A CHILD TO ME...

Human motivation extends beyond satisfying the basic needs we can be sure we share with other creatures. But the drive to meet the complex challenges we set ourselves must have similar origins. One recent Finnish study shows the ambition, also perhaps the limitations, of neuroscientists' efforts to understand complex social phenomena, comparing parental love with the feelings entrepreneurs have for companies they founded.

They probed the feelings of 21 fathers and 21 businessmen (there weren't any female entrepreneurs signed up) using questionnaires and brain scans. The MRI scans were used to compare whether there were areas of increased activity when they looked at pictures of either their own children or a similar unrelated child. You can't take a picture of a company, so the second comparison was between viewing the logo of the company the subjects had started and one from another outfit, chosen so it wasn't a known competitor.

Sure enough, a particular set of neural networks registered increased activity for both a father's own child and an entrepreneur's own company. And analysis of the scans showed a similar deactivation in certain areas – possibly associated with social assessments of other people. The researchers suggest the implication is that love is blind in both cases: just as parents may indulge their children, entrepreneurs may have an over-optimistic view of the performance of their young companies (they were 4.5 years old on average – the companies, that is).

So this is scientific confirmation, of a kind, of something already known: that people get emotionally attached to projects they have invested in, and feel pride if they succeed. Does this small study tell us more than that? Should prospective investors ask for a scan of a company founder's caudate nucleus to confirm their commitment to success at all costs? Many other brain regions have been highlighted in other studies of parents' responses to their children – the majority of them focused on mothers. Labelling the complex of feelings in play in the business focused side of this study "entrepreneurial love" is a bit of a stretch. And for investors, there are probably better ways to judge a new venture.

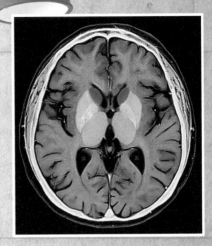

▲ In this particular study, the caudate nucleus (pink), found in the basal ganglia, was linked to feelings bound up with an entrepreneur's own firm, and his children.

CHAPTER 7

MEMORIES "R" US

MEMORIES ARE MADE OF THIS

When a machine blows a puff of air onto my eyeball during an eye test, I flinch, even though I know it's coming. Avoiding danger to the eyes is a powerful reflex. If a tone sounded just ahead of the puff, I would learn to flinch at the sound instead. It is a conditioned response, the kind first observed when Pavlov's dogs salivated at the sound of a bell signifying food.

If you try the puff-with-tone test on someone who has a missing or badly damaged hippocampus, they will learn the same response. There's a key difference. They'll have no recollection of the procedure that led to conditioning. Nevertheless, their nervous system "remembers" the tone that heralds the puff of air.

◄ The past fades – but not all of it, nor all at the same rate.

This is strong evidence that memory is not just one process. Our brains have several mechanisms for taking in new information in a way that makes it accessible to our future self. The

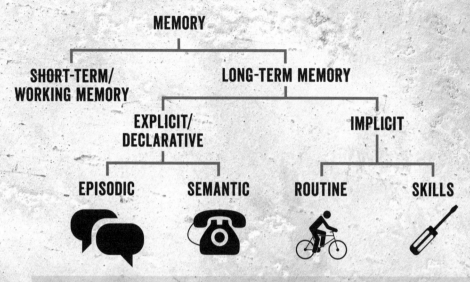

MEMORY

SHORT-TERM/ WORKING MEMORY

LONG-TERM MEMORY

EXPLICIT/ DECLARATIVE

IMPLICIT

EPISODIC **SEMANTIC** **ROUTINE** **SKILLS**

memory is more than one process

memories that sew together our identity, and allow us to manage our lives, are different from those that underpin learned skills or acquired responses.

There are various ways of dividing them up. There are conscious, or declarative memories. They allow us to describe to others what we think happened, or announce some piece of knowledge – we can only be sure that people have these. And there are implicit memories, which preserve skills and

routines, as well as fears and anxieties. The boundary isn't clear-cut – some things demand thought to begin with, then become automatic, like riding a bike.

Standard accounts of memory mention other subdivisions. Episodic and semantic memories both fall in the explicit, or declarative, category. Episodic memories are replays. The varied traces of past experiences – sensory and emotional – are reassembled. Semantic memories are of things learned as facts, like a list of capital cities, a phone number or a mathematical formula.

There are also categories based on timing. The fastest to decay is working memory, a kind of scratch pad where things like that phone number are kept for immediate use. Then there are short-term and long-term memories, with one long regarded as a prerequisite for the other.

HOW ALL THIS WORKS

There are splendid arguments about how all this works, on everything from the brain regions essential for each type of memory, to how they interact, and how memories are actually preserved. At the moment we know more about how memories are laid down initially than about how they endure or are accessed for recollection. Recalling an experience – the declarative part of declarative memory – is particularly tricky to study. Establishing a memory is (usually) the result of some set of external stimuli. Recall, though it may be prompted by some triggering stimulus, mainly involves scattered regions of the brain talking to each other. This makes it harder to devise simple experiments.

The most widely accepted basic theory is that information is encoded in the brain in the form of changes to synapses and to the strength of synaptic connections. We have a good idea how that comes about. The direct evidence for this being indispensable for at least some kinds of learning is strong. Is it the key to all aspects of memory? That's less certain.

Human memories seem special. We can speak about declarative memories, and our ability to learn new skills outstrips other brains. Our memory capacity must be finite, but is very large, as rare memory prodigies demonstrate. But we do not know whether these are abilities everyone might have, but cannot usually access. Nor is it clear whether memories that fade have actually disappeared, or may still be retained in the brain but are no longer easily accessible.

A PERMANENT PRESENT

He has been called the most important patient in the history of brain science. In 1953 Henry Molaison, then aged 27, had an extensive brain operation to relieve his epilepsy. A big chunk of his hippocampus was removed in both hemispheres. His seizures stopped. So, in a sense, did his life.

After the operation, he could no longer form long-term memories. His intelligence and personality were unaffected, and he could recall some of his life before the operation. But he managed to add very little to his long-term memory store. For Molaison (known as HM in scientific papers until his death in 2008) it was now always 1953.

His case was intensively studied, and weighed heavily against the then prevalent view that memories are stored in a scatter of locations throughout the brain. The effect of HM's giant lesion drew attention to the hippocampus's role in long-term memory. The evidence was fuzzy, as his surgeon removed portions of adjoining regions as well, and these are now also thought to be involved in processing memories. In addition, such surgery damages many major connective pathways.

Still, later cases of people with narrower hippocampal damage showed similar, less severe memory impairments. And HM, with the worst lesion, had the most wide-ranging amnesia.

He could learn new motor tasks, but the block on new declarative memories was fairly comprehensive. He did not recognize the face he saw in the mirror on waking, and introduced himself anew each day to researchers who worked with him for decades. One of the researchers, Suzanne Corkin of MIT, quoted him in her book *Permanent Present Tense* as remarking: "It's a funny thing – you just live and learn. I'm living and you're learning."

HM had appeared in thousands of scientific papers before he died. This is either a testament to neuroscientists' good use of an informative, if unfortunate, case study, or a sign of how little they once had to work with when reckoning with human memory. Nor is his contribution to science over. His brain is now preserved in 2,401 digitized slices made in a laboratory in San Diego, for further microanatomical study.

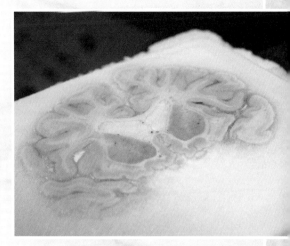

▲ HM's brain was frozen, then cut into ultra-thin slices, now archived.

▶ Suzanne Corkin.

MEMO TO RESEARCHERS: KEEP IT SIMPLE

The sea slug, *Aplysia californica*, has a simple life. Still, in its own fashion it can learn, and remember. Touch tho flap of skin that covers one of its gills, and the gill is drawn in. This defensive reaction can be modified by repeated touching, making it gradually weaker. Or you can apply an electric shock somewhere else, and it gets stronger.

In the early 1960s, US researchers Eric Kandel and Alden Spencer argued that if learning depended on modifying cell–cell interactions – on synaptic plasticity – it would be much easier to study in *Aplysia* than in more complex creatures. They had been grappling with the mammalian hippocampus but made little headway. The sea slug offered a small number – just 20,000 – of unusually large neurons, and changes in its reactions can involve fewer than 100.

The work they now began on *Aplysia* eventually included the ultimate simplification, one sensory neuron synapsing with one motor neuron in a laboratory dish. Using careful electrical and chemical prompts, they unveiled how learning works in their small mollusc. As usual, a neuron releases a neurotransmitter at

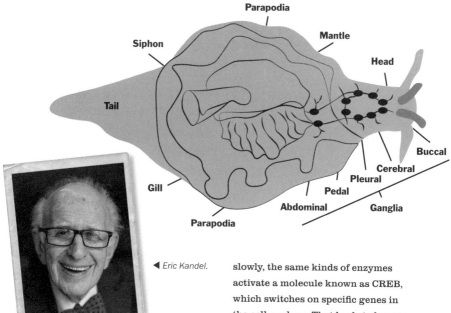

Parapodia

Siphon

Mantle

Head

Tail

Buccal

Cerebral

Pleural

Gill

Pedal

Abdominal

Ganglia

Parapodia

◀ *Eric Kandel.*

the synapse when it fires, glutamate in this case. Repeated firing produces less glutamate, and the next cell in the system gets a weaker signal.

When the creature is shocked, though, the signal gets stronger, by a roundabout route. The first neuron gets a shot of another transmitter, serotonin, from a different axon. That quickly activates an enzyme that makes small changes to proteins, and modifies ion channels in the cell membrane. More

slowly, the same kinds of enzymes activate a molecule known as CREB, which switches on specific genes in the cell nucleus. That leads to larger modifications of the synapse, and to new synapses between the same pair of cells. Changes in the post-synaptic cell complete the process, producing a stronger connection that is long-lasting.

Choosing a simple model system to shed light on a complex problem is a standard research strategy in biology, but has rarely proved so fruitful. Kandel, who shared the Nobel Prize in Physiology or Medicine in 2000, described his move to the sea slug as "a leap of faith for which I have been rewarded beyond my fondest hopes".

A COINCIDENCE DETECTOR

Knowing what you are looking for is a big help when working on complex systems like the ones neuroscientists grapple with. The sea slug work quickly led to similar findings in other species, including mammals.

The story there centres on a special kind of post-synaptic receptor. It is called the NMDA receptor, for N-methyl-D-aspartate. That molecule does stick to it, but in the cell it responds to the neurotransmitter glutamate. Its special feature is that it is an ion channel, but normally stays blocked, by a magnesium ion. It is unblocked if the cell it sits in is depolarized by lots of synaptic signals, either from multiple incoming synapses or from fast repeats of action potentials.

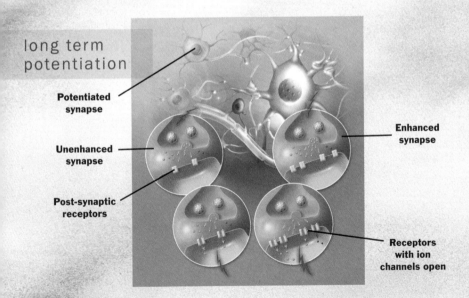

long term potentiation

Potentiated synapse

Unenhanced synapse

Post-synaptic receptors

Enhanced synapse

Receptors with ion channels open

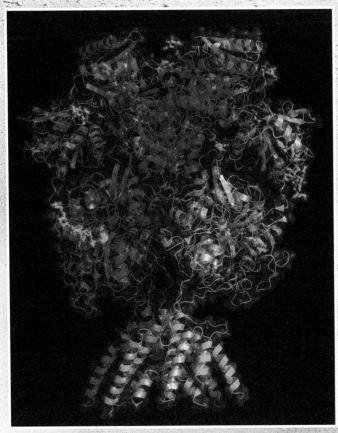

◀ This 3D model of one type of NMDA receptor, from the Cold Spring Harbor Lab in the US, has been compared to a hot air balloon. Glutamate binds to a region on the balloon, outside the cell. The "basket", underneath, is inside.

They also make the receiving cell fire an action potential. The combination makes the NMDA receptor a coincidence detector. It registers when two connected neurons fire at the same time.

Unblocking the NMDA ion channel triggers an inflow of calcium ions, and then a cascade of cellular events that strengthen and then remodel the synaptic link between the two cells. The

whole sequence is known as long-term potentiation. A crucial step is gene activation by CREB, the same molecule identified in the sea slug. And like the sea slug system the response to the NMDA switch has both fast and slow components, with the slower ones dependent on gene action.

There are more complications, such as arranging for molecules manufactured by newly activated genes to act only on synapses that have been "tagged" for reinforcement – otherwise every connection the cell makes would end up stronger. But these basic findings look robust. Most recently, CREB has been shown to help link memories of separate events, by selecting links between neurons that encode memories for reinforcement. This will stand as one mechanism by which synaptic connections are reinforced, a key part of many kinds of learning and memory throughout life.

Altogether, it is one of the nicest examples to date of cellular neuroscience dovetailing with a molecular understanding of what is happening. It is also a belated testament to the insights of the Canadian psychologist Donald Hebb. In 1949, in his book *The Organization of Behavior*, he proposed how a basic part of learning could work: "When an axon of cell A is near enough to excite a cell B and repeatedly or persistently takes part in firing it, some growth process or metabolic change takes place in one or both cells such that A's efficiency, as one of the cells firing B, is increased." Short version: cells that fire together, wire together. The NMDA receptor system appears to do just that, and the junctions that feature this brand of receptor are dubbed Hebbian synapses.

◀ *Crystals of pure NMDA.*

A MOUSE WITH AN ELEPHANT'S MEMORY

Just as brain lesions help locate regions that contribute to a particular function, so taking away a key molecule can help show its role in the cell. The difference with molecules is that you can arrange an oversupply as well.

Ideally, this can be done through genetic tweaks, and much neuroscience research adopts this approach, usually in mice. In 1999, Princeton researcher Joe Tsien showed that giving mice extra copies of the gene for their NMDA receptor made them better at remembering.

He already knew that reducing NMDA production made learning harder, and that it gets harder to activate the receptors as the animals age. The mice

with enhanced NMDA confirmed its role in memory by showing improved recollection on simple tests, such as whether they explored a new object in preference to one they had seen before, and faster learning.

The "Doogie" mice, named after a super-smart character in a TV series of the time, made news around the world, and raised hopes of future treatments for failing memories. However, enthusiasm was dampened by the subsequent finding that they also showed a heightened sensitivity to chronic pain. Like a drug, a gene boost is a blunt instrument for acting on the intricacy of tissues with billions of cells that often use the same molecules for many different things.

▶ Joe Tsien with one of his experimental mice.

FROM NEUROTRANSMITTERS TO NEUROMODULATORS

The sea slug led the way to understanding how having two neurotransmitters can enlarge the options for neuron action, and the NMDA system has similar properties that are fairly easy to summarize.

A model system from another marine organism, however, has helped show just how intricate adjustments to neuron action can be. Eve Marder of Brandeis University began working on simple neural circuits that control stomach contractions in lobsters and crabs in the late 1960s.

She soon found that, in a separable circuit of just 30 neurons, there were again two neurotransmitters – glutamate and acetylcholine – in play, and that they had different effects depending on local cellular circumstance.

Further work showed that a host of other molecules affected the output from individual neurons, and neural circuits, and could be used to manipulate them experimentally. Her lab currently lists 27 different circulating hormones that can affect the same neurons, and another 27 "locally delivered neuromodulators", including neurotransmitters and other more recently discovered small molecules that originate from nearby neurons.

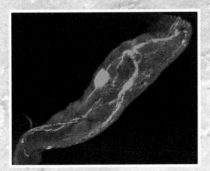

◀ One of the neurons in the ganglion that control a lobster's stomach.

◀ *A larval lobster.*

This gives the simple network enormous scope for tiny variations in activity. The working assumption is that subtle neuromodulation is the rule rather than the exception in more complex nervous systems, too. Neuromodulators are generally slow-acting by comparison with neurotransmitters, but affect how easy it is to get neurons to respond to a dendritic input or inputs – how excitable they are – as well as how much neurotransmitter is released when they fire and the pattern of firing.

This fills out the picture of neuroplasticity beyond the basic ingredients of the NMDA system, allowing neural circuits to deliver much richer dynamics than researchers used to think possible.

But brains have a powerful need for regularity, too. The main circuit studied in the lobster gut maintains a pattern-generated rhythm (like walking or breathing) that is unvarying. Later development of the work, combining computer-controlled signalling to cultured neurons and computer-modelling of neuronal networks, has shown how circuits can go on delivering the same output even when individual neurons are altered in various ways. The same evolved mechanisms thus contribute to flexibility, when needed, and to stability.

CELLS THAT KNOW, BUT DON'T TELL

We have a good idea how many kinds of memories are acquired, and where they are processed. Still, storage and retrieval pose many unanswered questions. And some of the things we think we understand may yet turn out to be wrong.

One is the relation between short-term and long-term memory. The categories look real. Many things we retain for a few days or weeks, but only a fraction end up as memories accessible, or amenable to reconstruction, for a lifetime. But the belief that long-term memories are a selection of items that have first been stored in short-term memory, in a two-step process, was shaken in 2017.

▼ *A single hippocampal neuron.*

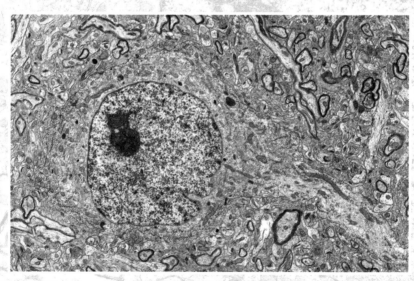

Researchers led by Takashi Kitamura in Tokyo used optogenetics to probe when memories became active in different parts of the brain in mice. They found that there were cells in the hippocampus and the cortex encoding traces of the memory created by an electric shock. However, both were there in less than a day, contradicting the idea that short-term memories are laid down in the hippocampus, and transferred later to the prefrontal cortex for long-term storage and retrieval.

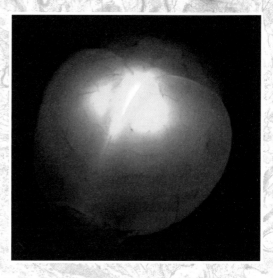

They infer that short- and long-term memories are laid down at the same time. This was not apparent before, the experiment indicated, because the cortical memory is not accessible at first – it was only revealed when activated by turning on an optogenetic switch in the neurons involved.

Extended observation showed that the initially "silent" memory cells in the cortex matured and became active over about two weeks. The hippocampal cells did the opposite, gradually falling silent. They could still be activated by the experimenters, though, suggesting that traces of short-term memories remained.

▲ *A tiny LED implanted in a mouse brain can activate sensitized neurons.*

The study also traced the contribution of cells in part of the amygdala, which stored some aspects of the event – the initial shock – and connected to both the cortex and the hippocampus.

If the work is confirmed, it may lead to major revisions of theories of memory formation and partition.

IN SEARCH OF THE ENGRAM

The strengthening of synaptic connections is a likely solution to a key problem for the neuroscience of memory. It was formulated back in 1904 by the German Richard Semon. An individual memory, he said, must leave a physical trace in the brain, an engram.

The virtue of coining a new word was that it didn't imply any theory about what an engram actually is. There have been plenty of suggestions since, from molecules to resonating circuits to an idea that enjoyed a brief vogue in the 1970s, holograms.

The changes in brains that represent memories must have similar properties to memories themselves. They are durable, exquisitely selective, sometimes reversible, and can be accessed fairly easily – sometimes consciously, sometimes not. The various ways synapses are strengthened seem a good fit. The specific tags on synapses that mark them out for reinforcement can be identified. And there are complementary processes in which synapses grow weaker, or are destroyed. So strengthening synapses does not spiral out of control, with everything ending up connected to everything else.

Most contemporary accounts of memory do begin with neuron firing patterns and altered synapses. There are confident references to "engram cells", and their activation does indeed correlate with memory retrieval. Still, there are significant details to worry about. Long-term memories may need specific changes in dendritic spines, and their many synapses. And there are suggestions that synaptic alteration is crucial for memory retrieval, but not the key to preserving information.

Some theorists still focus on other parts of the neuron. There are epigenetic changes – small modifications to DNA – that some think might be significant for preserving

▶ The secret of memory lies in the synapse – but perhaps not only there.

199

memories. There is evidence that short genetic messages, in the form of RNA molecules transcribed from DNA, can be transferred between neurons, or even between neurons and glial cells. The discovery of newborn neurons in the hippocampus also comes into the mix – any synapses they make are new, by definition. And the actual timing of neuronal firing, the pattern of spikes sent down an axon, may be important during recall of stored memories.

So, is the engram a set of synapses, a connected set of cells, a pattern of neural firing, or – an old school idea – a molecule or molecules?

Perhaps proteins, or even DNA are involved. But most molecules, and most cells, are continually broken down and replaced, so any theory has to explain how long term memories can last for decades. It must be some kind of pattern that endures, like the geography of a city that is always being rebuilt piecemeal. Could it be the scaffolding that locates synaptic receptors, perhaps? Something to do with the arrangement of microtubules inside neurons? It is hard to find any aspect of the microstructure of the brain that has not been offered as a candidate for memory storage. One further suggestion for the final repository of memory is a structural change in the "perineuronal net", a term for lots of connected molecules in the extracellular matrix that fills the tiny spaces between brain cells. Perhaps we'll see a general theory of memory that combines all of these contributions into one system, but it isn't here yet.

▼ Rebuild a city, and the street map usually stays the same: a different kind of memory?

"If the brain really computed the way most people think, it would boil in a minute."

MOLECULAR MEMORY?

A challenge to the focus on neural connection, and the spike trains that pass down axons, as the main mechanism for accessing memories is that they carry a high-energy cost.

Charles Gallistel of Rutgers University insists that memory as an information system must involve computations, and that making that happen by altering patterns of axon firing would use far too much energy. "If the brain really computed the way most people think, it would boil in a minute," he argues. The alternative? In his view, molecules. As he puts it: "Compute with chemistry, it's cheaper."

More formally, he argues that the computation is happening inside brain cells, "performed by intracellular neurochemistry operating on information stored in cell-intrinsic molecular machinery". One day, he believes, we will find that memory "looks like a gene that experience can write to". For now, it is a minority view, but it is not possible yet to rule it out.

REMEMBERING OR REINVENTING?

One thing that is certain about memory is that there are crucial trade-offs in making it work. The brain has to find ways of preserving information using elements that are subject to constant change. Protein molecules are destroyed and replaced. Synapses get rebuilt. Neurons often endure, but their connections change.

▼ *Memories might feel like movies, but they are not stored on anything like the frames in a strip of film.*

Yet memories persist. Adults' earliest memories may reach back as far as their three-year-old selves – and some researchers claim evidence of recall from even earlier. Even working memory lasts much longer than most events inside cells, where a millisecond is a long time.

These constraints influence thinking about memory storage and retrieval. We know that stored memories of experiences involve numerous distinct regions of the brain. Recollecting the experience must involve bringing these separate traces together. It seems the neural activations this requires also change some connections, so that associations are strengthened. Just as neuroplasticity allows memories to be laid down in the first place, it refreshes them when they are brought back into awareness. In this fashion, a detailed recollection is not simply read from a store, but reconstructed. It feels like a movie, but the metaphor is misleading unless the movie is partly reshot and edited each time it is viewed.

The brain is also a noisy place, electrically and chemically, and memory inevitably decays.

And the memories we feel most sure of, because they are revisited so often, may become less accurate, because repeated retrieval tips the balance between recollection and reconstruction.

We know this can happen because of recent investigations of false memory. People can profess vivid memories, sometimes of traumatic events, that turn out to be inadvertent inventions. Distinguishing such self-deception from genuine memories, especially "recovered" memories, of the same kind of event is worryingly problematic.

Can the science help? Only a little so far. Experiments have shown some differences in functional magnetic resonance imaging scans when "true" or "false" memories are activated, but traumatic life events cannot be replicated in the lab.

It is also possible to implant false memories (of a much simpler kind) in mice, but this relies on external intervention by researchers, using electrodes, so is of limited use in probing how they might be internally generated.

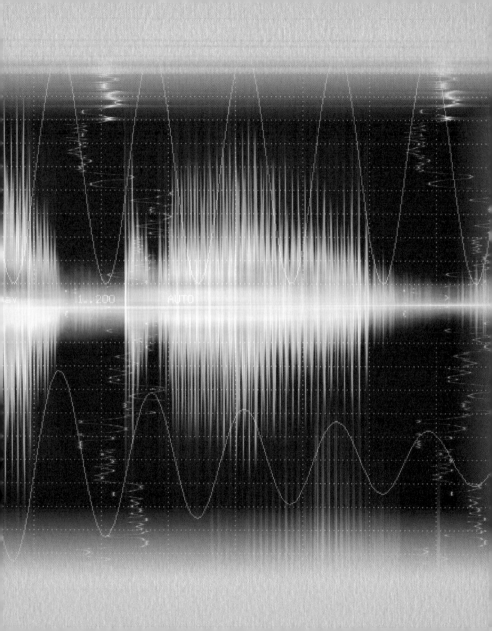

CHAPTER 8

IT'S GOOD TO TALK

THE TALKING APE

▼ Noam Chomsky.

Language, which sets us apart from other creatures, is one of the most intriguing capacities of our brains. Trained primates – chimps, bonobos – can learn to use signs, but the richness of spoken language is a human monopoly. And while words are not always the origin of the thought, we certainly put most of our thoughts into words.

▼ Nim Chimpsky, who learned a small portion of American Sign Language in the 1970s.

By the same token, investigating the neuroscience of language has been unusually difficult. Only human brains can be studied. Accidental lesions were the main source of information for many decades. They have been supplemented by psychological experiments, electrical stimulation and, more recently, by brain scans and computer modelling.

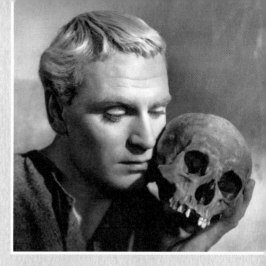

We are born without language. It has to be learned, and there is a critical period for doing so (see Chapter 3). But are we programmed to learn? The dominant view, originally proposed by Noam Chomsky, is that the bare bones of language – basic grammatical structures – are innate. These structures, presumably built into neural circuitry at birth, are clothed with the details of individual languages dictated by local culture.

▲ To be, or not to be ... Shakespeare's working vocabulary was exceptionally large.

There is plenty of evidence that fits this idea, from linguistics and genetics, but it is not universally accepted. It might be that language is acquired via a general pattern recognition ability that allows growing brains to learn by following statistical associations. This cannot yet account for all the features of language learning, but it has what is normally considered a scientific plus point: it's a more economical theory. We know that this kind of learning goes on, and we understand something of how synaptic modification helps it happen.

Meanwhile, research tries to tie together language comprehension with language production – how we hear a stream of sound as a sequence of individual words, and can say our own sentences out loud – as well as probing how we learn the more obviously not innate business of reading and writing.

LOCATING LANGUAGE

Brain lesions that pointed to language areas were the beginning of modern cerebral localization in the 19th century, when actual anatomy succeeded phrenology as the basis for dividing up the grey matter into functional areas (see Chapter 1).

The two cortical regions discovered by Paul Broca and Karl Wernicke, usually found in the left hemisphere, are still labelled with their names, but their functions are no longer seen as clear-cut. Some people with lesions in Broca's area do not have Broca's aphasia, for example, and vice versa. In fact, the brains of Broca's first two patients are still preserved in

▲ The brain of one of Broca's patients. Even after 100 years, a preserved brain can yield new information.

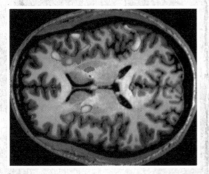

◀ An fMRI scan from a study of sentence completion.

Paris, and have now been examined using magnetic resonance imaging (MRI). Scans showed other brain regions that were damaged, as well as decay in important connecting channels.

Close study of others who have lost some or all of their language abilities, most often stroke patients, has shown many more details of small brain regions that are vital for listening and talking.

Put them together and you can make a rough outline of the main links in language processing in the brain. It looks like this.

language processing in the brain

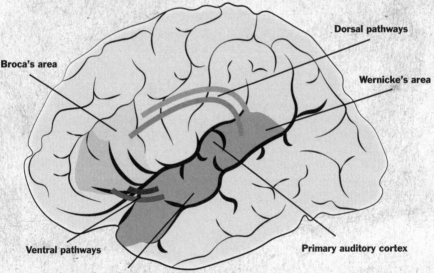

One of two dorsal pathways (pale blue) connects Wernicke's area and the auditory areas – both located in the superior temporal gyrus – with the pre-motor cortex, and is involved in speaking. The other links these areas with Broca's area, and is vital for processing sentence structures. The ventral pathways are important for processing speech. The details of the various pathways are still being refined.

FROM WORDS TO SENTENCES

Study of brains and language was mostly anatomical for a long while. But, like brain science in general, neurolinguistics is being illuminated by improvements in technique that bring researchers closer to actual language processing.

A striking example published in 2017 takes neuroscience beyond simple word recognition to the next level of language – where meaning is extracted from strings of words in what is effectively an unlimited number of sentences.

The research, by a Franco-American team, involved electrical recording from inside the brains of people as they read a series of test sentences. The dozen subjects were epileptics who agreed to insertion of electrodes in language areas before surgery to help their condition.

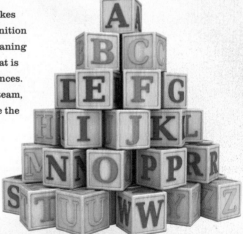

INTO PHRASES

Then they read sentences of increasing length in their own language – English or French – one word at a time, as the research team recorded brain activity.

Language areas showed an increase in activity as each word appeared. The interesting part was when a few words completed a phrase. Psychologists already know that sentence structure is understood by "chunking" words into groups to make phrases, themselves combined according to grammatical rules.

In this experiment, brain activity dropped each time words could be clumped together to form a phrase, then picked up again as more words appeared.

The interpretation is that individual words are held in linguistic working memory, until they can be merged in this way. At that stage, several "units" of working memory become one, and the demand on the brain is momentarily reduced. So in these languages, at least, readers process in this way as they go.

Overall, each additional word or multi-word phrase contributed roughly the same amount of additional brain activity in this exercise. The finding does not cover the furthest reaches of linguistic complexity, when people may write (if not speak) paragraph-length sentences. But as far as it goes it meshes with the models that assume language is decoded hierarchically, with the brain having an ability to "nest" phrases inside one another. Some education systems teach kids to diagram sentences this way to instil rules of grammar. But the brain seems to learn it automatically.

WHY YOU CAN READ THIS

Even if language proves to be innate, reading clearly is not. And the way in which learning to read alters the brain is a great example of how the brain and nervous system coevolve with culture, each accommodating to the constraints and demands of the other.

Stanislas Dehaene, one of the designers of the sentence decoding experiment, and colleagues in Paris, showed some years ago that reading depends on a small portion of the visual cortex. It is in more or less the same location in all readers scanned, no matter which writing system is read, and becomes active in the same hemisphere as other language abilities.

The region involved is connected to the centre of the retina, the fovea, where cells are closely spaced and visual discrimination is most acute. It normally responds to small and relatively simple shapes, or parts of shapes, that allow

us to analyse scenes and objects around us. As we learn to read, Dehaene believes, it adapts to recognize the shapes of the alphabet or character set in question.

He suggests that, although ways of writing vary from our own familiar alphabet to the array of symbols in Chinese, they all combine elementary shapes which the brain can already register. Each writing system evolved, he speculates, through exploration of various combinations of these shapes as symbols for words, or sounds. Our brain allowed this cultural invention because it is flexible enough to reassign some of the neurons involved to a new task. It also limits the forms the invention can take. Only a limited set of shapes that we can already sense can be included in a writing system.

As we learn to read, the visual word form area, as it is known, becomes more active, and reorganizes its connections with brain regions involved with spoken language. According to Dehaene, "the acquisition of literacy consists in creating a new visual input pathway into this language network." At the same time, the visual word form area in the language-dominant hemisphere becomes less responsive to faces, which are subsequently recognized mainly in the other (usually the right) hemisphere.

SPEECH, SPEECH

Speech falls on the ear as continuous variations in the vibration of air molecules, like any other sound. Yet these particular sounds are usually divided up in the right places to indicate that we are hearing words. We hear "catalogue", not "cat, a, log".

We have yet to work out exactly how this is done. Comparing what is happening in the brain with machine-based approaches to extracting words from sounds is one new approach to finding out – an example of the increasing cross-fertilization between neuroscience and computer science.

Computer-based speech recognition systems have got better and better – just ask Siri. They can be introduced into neuroscientists' investigations in several ways. Experiments generally focus on data from electroencephalogram (EEG) or magnetoencephalography (MEG) scans. They are noninvasive and, unlike MRI, they can track changes in the brain fast enough to keep up with the rate of changes in sounds during speech. They provide data on collections of neurons that fire together. A few projects have used direct recording from electrodes introduced into the brains of surgical patients.

Artificial speech recognition systems are trained on vast amounts of data. They decode what is said statistically, using models of the probabilities of a word appearing

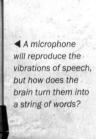

◀ A microphone will reproduce the vibrations of speech, but how does the brain turn them into a string of words?

given the ones already registered, and databases of pronunciation that break words down into distinct speech sound units – or "phones".

Such systems have been used to produce simple "brain-to-text" read-outs, by applying them to much smaller amounts of data from electrode recording during speech. One long-term aim is to build a system that can generate text from inner speech, without sound.

Other researchers compare patterns in the signals obtained from EEGs and MEGs during processing of spoken words with those that an artificial speech recognition system produces at various stages in its work on the same input. They examine computer analyses of brain image data, related to a particular vocal input, alongside analyses of the operation of a computer system set up for the same task.

Combining disciplines like this promises to improve speech recognition systems, for example by dividing continuous sound input in more natural ways, as well as shedding light on neural speech processing.

▼ The human throat, anatomized in the 17th century.

COULD LIGHT-BULB MOMENTS BE REAL?

You're watching a cartoon character with a problem. A light bulb materializes above their head. They have an idea! One of the more eye-catching recent brain scanning efforts suggests that "light-bulb moments" could be real – well, almost.

Jack Gallant's lab at the University of California, Berkeley, published a remarkable map of the human brain in 2016 that displays which parts of the cortex respond to individual words. The result, which can be explored in an interactive display on the web, evoked enthusiasm and criticism. It is a state-of-the-art contribution to cognitive neuroscience. But maybe it is also an example of data-driven redescription that produces pretty pictures but doesn't really tell us much about how the brain actually works.

It certainly looks very impressive. A bit of detail about how the map was made gives a good sense of how brain-imaging data is treated to produce such powerful imagery.

The work develops previous studies aiming to map "semantic space". A researcher in Gallant's lab, Alexander Huth, signed up half a dozen people to listen to audio recordings of stories – that used around 3,000 different words – for two hours, their brains being scanned all the while by an MRI machine.

The scans recorded brain regions that appeared more active, indicated by increased blood flow, for each individual word. The lengthy scan allowed good resolution, down to small pieces of tissue known as voxels (like a pixel, but a unit of volume).

Then came more elaborate processing. The direct scan-and-word data was combined with a database which used a large set of texts to figure out how often 10,000 words – the original 3,000 plus another 7,000 – occur together with around 1,000 common words. This defined a "space" in which word associations are mapped in detail, and was used to predict where any of the full set of 10,000 words would have lit up the scanner, if the listeners had heard them.

A further step reduced the big word set to just four dimensions, related to their wider associations. Three of these were then used to colour the overall map.

That is where the demands of cute presentation perhaps outweigh scientific considerations, as it is hard to say what those "dimensions" actually signify, apart from their arbitrarily assigned colours. But they sure do make the map look prettier.

That ought not to take away from the fact that the mapping of words onto brain regions is fascinating, as well as endlessly suggestive. And there are two large findings that put much previous work on brains and language in a different light. Many findings suggest that language processing is localized to particular brain regions, and generally in only one hemisphere. Yet this map indicates that more or less the entire cortex is involved in interpreting word meanings. And here there is no hemispheric division. Also unexpected was the finding from this small group (six plus Huth himself) that the maps derived from their scans were broadly similar. Further work on more diverse subjects, and speakers of different languages, will follow.

Beyond that, it seems the map delivers more detail than researchers, or laypeople, can really make sense of at this stage in our understanding of the language system in the brain.

▲ This image of the cortex is overlaid with individual words that produce responses in small regions of cells – all over the brain.

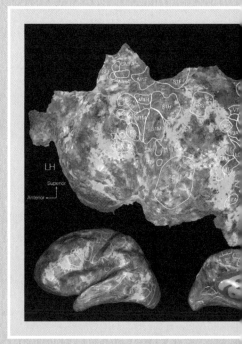

There are patterns here that relate in some way to the really important thing about words – their meanings. But what do the patterns themselves mean? Answering that requires some developments in theory that are hard to envisage at the moment. As one researcher commented: "Based on results such as these, it's pretty unlikely that we would change our conceptualizations of semantics or the neural basis of language processing."

Still, the cortex with words mapped onto it, while looking a little like souped-up phrenology, is a technical achievement far beyond the reach of earlier generations of neuroscientists. And it yields an image of the brain that fires the imagination. Who knows where it might lead?

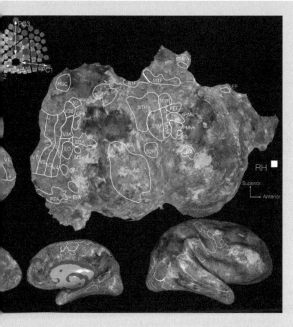

a new kind of brain atlas

These composite images from the language-mapping study show how responses to words assigned to different categories are distributed over the cerebral cortex – shown in both 3D views, and (in the centre) flattened out for easier analysis. The full image set is interactive.

CHAPTER 9

MANIPULATING THE BRAIN

FEELING GOOD

Like emotions, pleasure and pain are linked to the body but experienced in the brain. Most of us would prefer to maximize the pleasure and minimize the pain. However we try to do that, we are acting on the brain. That means affecting the chemical and electrical events happening, moment by moment, in neural networks.

History documents many different cultures' habits of stimulating the brain with chemicals. Now we have additional options for intervening directly in the electrical traffic, too. We cannot yet do either in a tightly controlled way, with reliable results. But we can begin to see how that might happen.

Underlying such ideas is a well-supported set of results about how and why the brain generates pleasure. As usual, the findings sit in an evolutionary context. Our pleasures were originally a way to motivate us to do things that promoted survival and reproduction. Less usually, the current story about which parts of the brain speak the language of pleasure is accepted by virtually everyone. It doubtless isn't the whole story, but is almost certainly correct as far as it goes.

It begins in the 1950s with an accidental finding from experiments using rodents wired with electrodes deep in their brains. Researchers in Canada found a small brain region that rats, allowed to activate a small current

◀ Sadly, feeling good and being good for you do not always overlap.

there, would stimulate endlessly, to the exclusion of all
else. A wired rat, pressing the magic lever up to 7,000
times an hour before exhaustion set in, was one of the
dominant images of brain research through the 1960s.
Further work mapped a set of interconnected regions,
dubbed pleasure centres, that have a powerful role to play
in regulating behaviour. A new idea at the time, this is
now common wisdom. And we have good ideas about the
workings of the system, in some detail. Orgasmatron-
style experiments on humans are unacceptable (though
one or two have been tried), but there's good evidence the
basic system works similarly in all mammals.

▲ Sometimes just the
promise of pleasure
keeps us going.

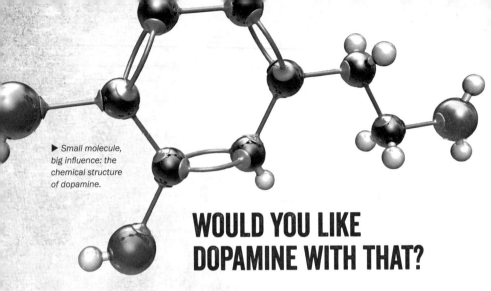

► *Small molecule, big influence: the chemical structure of dopamine.*

WOULD YOU LIKE DOPAMINE WITH THAT?

Electrical and chemical analysis of the pleasure centres indicates that a key player is a small region in the midbrain called the ventral tegmental area (VTA to its friends). It has neurons with axon connections to several other parts of the brain, including the prefrontal cortex, amygdala, hippocampus and a region called the striatum. All receive dopamine, the activating neurotransmitter, when VTA neurons fire. But the most important connections for feeling good appear to link the VTA's dopamine release to an area next to the striatum known as the nucleus accumbens.

The VTA decides what signals to pass on by weighing inputs from excitatory synapses linked to the prefrontal cortex – which release glutamate – and inhibitory synapses – releasing gamma-amino-butyric-acid (GABA) – coming back from the nucleus accumbens.

The core idea is that increasing dopamine release from the VTA, especially in the nucleus accumbens, equates to pleasure. The rat pawing a lever to get the electrical benefit is actually seeking a dose of neurotransmitter in the right place. And so, in the simplest view, are we when we do whatever it is that makes us feel good. A large collection of experiments – with controlled electrical stimulation, injection of dopamine or its precursors, or chemicals that block dopamine action – fit this basic hypothesis.

The VTA's connections to other brain areas open up theorizing about links between emotion and memory and pleasurable experiences. The action of the other neurotransmitters on VTA neurons gives the whole system more flexibility. And the longer-term plasticity of synapses that figures in current ideas about memory – strengthening some connections while weakening others – allows more elaborate explanations: of how some pleasures loom larger in our lives at different times, how habits are laid down, and how some once pleasurable habits become addictions even though the rewards felt in the brain have faded away. It's far from a complete account of human behaviour, which is much more complex than a rodent's. But neuroscience does have the outlines of a general theory of pleasure.

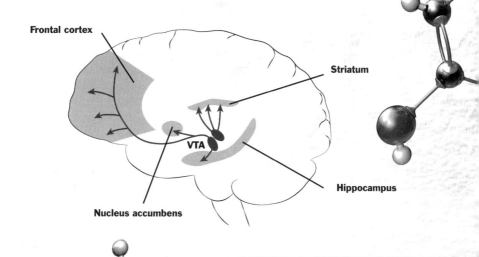

Frontal cortex

Striatum

VTA

Hippocampus

Nucleus accumbens

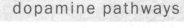

dopamine pathways

225

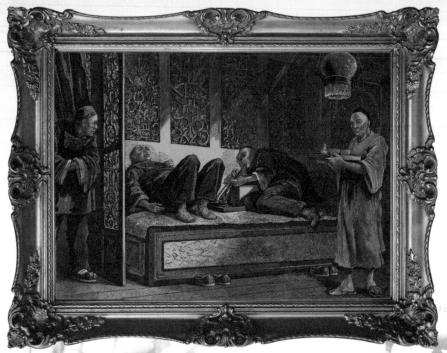

▲ An artist's rendering of a 19th-century opium den in San Francisco.

DRUGS WITH A HISTORY

Some drugs used by pleasure seekers have been around for centuries, some are brand new. All act on the chemical traffic between neurons, one way or another. In most cases we have a good idea how they work. However appealing their effects, all are blunt instruments to apply to something as precious and intricately organized as your own brain, but millions do. And they have also yielded useful clues about how the brain works.

Recent neuroscience has shed new light on old drugs. Opium, in use for thousands of years, is extracted from a poppy plant. Its active ingredient, morphine, was isolated early in the 19th century, and its chemical structure solved properly a century later. Heroin is a simple chemical derivative of morphine which is soluble in oils and fats, allowing it to pass more easily across cell membranes. Both produce a complex of effects, including easing aches and pains, detachment from worldly cares, and a general euphoria.

But how? Chemical hints began to emerge in the 1950s. Small alterations in molecular structure could produce far more potent drugs, or block drug action altogether – circumstantial evidence for a specific receptor for morphine. That receptor was finally isolated in 1972, when Candace Pert managed to get a highly radioactive morphine blocker to stick to receptors long enough to fish them out of homogenized brain cells. Her research was funded as part of US President Nixon's "war on drugs", a response to heroin addiction among returning Vietnam veterans. The war on drugs was never won but secured a small victory for neuroscience.

That triggered a search for a chemical answer to a now obvious question: why was the receptor there? There must be some previously unknown messenger in the brain destined for the lock that morphine's chemical key happened to fit. The race to identify the first of these home-grown opiates was won in 1976 by a group in Scotland.

NEUROCHEMISTRY, OLD STYLE

How many pigs' brains would you like today? Well, I can get around 20 into this dry ice crate on the back of my bike...

The high-tech neuroscience of the 21st century often piles up data fast, even though it may be hard to interpret. But much brain research in the past was a hard slog – like the isolation of the first of what turned out to be a family of peptide molecules that use the morphine receptor.

It began in an Aberdeen slaughterhouse, where researcher John Hughes collected pig heads so he could remove their brains. Back in the lab, the frozen pig brains – others used calf brains – had to be mashed up and crudely processed with acetone, to get fats out of the way. The remaining protein soup was gradually reduced to leave behind a mixture of small molecules, one of which might be the target.

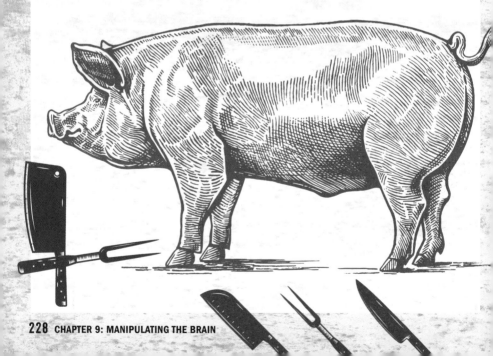

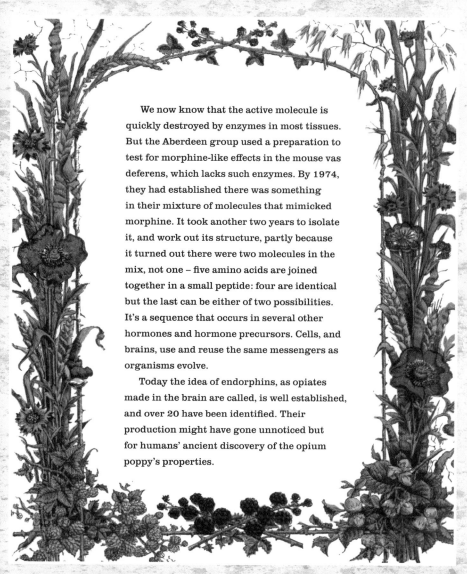

We now know that the active molecule is quickly destroyed by enzymes in most tissues. But the Aberdeen group used a preparation to test for morphine-like effects in the mouse vas deferens, which lacks such enzymes. By 1974, they had established there was something in their mixture of molecules that mimicked morphine. It took another two years to isolate it, and work out its structure, partly because it turned out there were two molecules in the mix, not one – five amino acids are joined together in a small peptide: four are identical but the last can be either of two possibilities. It's a sequence that occurs in several other hormones and hormone precursors. Cells, and brains, use and reuse the same messengers as organisms evolve.

Today the idea of endorphins, as opiates made in the brain are called, is well established, and over 20 have been identified. Their production might have gone unnoticed but for humans' ancient discovery of the opium poppy's properties.

WHERE THE ACTION IS

The search for brain molecules that they may mimic, and receptors that embrace them, has yielded details of how humans' old drugs of choice work. A good proportion tie in with the pleasure centres, as their effects suggest. One way or another, they amplify the action of dopamine in areas connected to the VTA region.

Morphine does this indirectly, by reducing the release of the inhibitory neurotransmitter GABA. That results in more excited VTA neurons, which send out more dopamine to their targets.

Cannabis has an active ingredient, tetrahydrocannabinol, which binds to receptors that normally recognize molecules made in the brain, and so produces feel-good effects in the same way.

Cocaine, by contrast, blocks a transporter that mops up dopamine by taking it back into the presynaptic cell. So the pleasure-giving neurotransmitter hangs around longer and has a stronger effect on its targets. The artificial latecomers, amphetamines, do the same.

Nicotine finds another way to increase dopamine release from the VTA that involves binding to specific receptors. In this case, they are a class of acetylcholine receptors that increase glutamate release on the input

side of VTA neurons, enhancing their excitation.

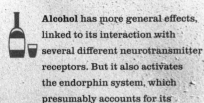

Alcohol has more general effects, linked to its interaction with several different neurotransmitter receptors. But it also activates the endorphin system, which presumably accounts for its moderate euphoric effect.

FOR THE LOVE OF CAFFEINE

Even caffeine, which achieves most of its diverse effects by binding to a ubiquitous receptor for the common cellular chemical adenosine, has its ways of affecting dopamine levels.

The world's favourite psychoactive drug is most often thought of as a general booster, increasing alertness and warding off sleep. It does those things mainly by blocking receptors for adenosine that are present on most cells, including neurons.

Proteins that bind small molecules often evolve from existing receptors, and adenosine receptors are structurally similar to other kinds, so some of them form stable assemblies with various types of dopamine receptors.

When caffeine hits the adenosine binding bit of one of these protein conglomerates, it changes shape in a way that also affects the dopamine binding portion.

In this fashion, as well as its wide-ranging effects on blood pressure, urination, heart rate, and alertness, caffeine has its effect on dopamine in the striatum and nucleus accumbens. And a morning cup of coffee can induce a feeling of wellbeing as well as alertness.

THE PLEASURABLE PATH TO ADDICTION

Drug use, and chances of addiction, vary a lot according to time, place and temperament. But research on the brain regions that communicate rewards with dopamine as the messenger – much of it using rats that self-administer chemicals instead of electrical stimulation – has now built up a working overall theory of addiction.

Chemical addiction is more than a habit. It involves a shift from an occasional "take it or leave it" use of a drug to dependence, with strong cravings on withdrawal. At the same time, the repeat user comes to tolerate the drug – needing larger doses and feeling less effect. And there are powerful associations that can trigger relapse in recovering addicts.

All this takes time, and not everyone becomes addicted. (Nicotine is the most alluring chemical, with 80 per cent of smokers becoming

addicted, more than twice the proportion of addicts among those who inject heroin.)

One way to understand this is to treat addiction as something the brain learns. And there is good evidence that it changes the brain in similar ways to other kinds of learning and memory (see Chapter 7).

For example, long-term potentiation of some excitatory synapses in the VTA happens after a single dose of cocaine, and can also be induced by morphine, nicotine and alcohol. The effect is specific to addictive drugs, and to this portion of the brain. Longer-term effects include downrating of some inhibitory synapses.

Such changes could expedite dopamine release by strengthening connections between the VTA, parts of the cortex and the amygdala, laying down associations that help establish addiction. Repeated use of these drugs causes changes in the regions that receive input from the VTA which tend to *reduce* dopamine release when VTA neurons fire, which seems a plausible mechanism for developing tolerance.

These are the rudiments of a general theory of addiction. That extends beyond drugs to cover pathological attachments to gambling, sweet foods, or sex. In that light, behaviour that brings pleasure is indirect chemical manipulation of the brain. By the same token, efforts to overcome addictions – of all kinds – tend to require long-term application because they involve learning a new pattern of behaviour.

▼ *Slot machines are cunningly designed to produce a behaviour pattern that repeats.*

DRUGGED BY LOVE?

If addiction is harmful, can obsession be benign? And how can we draw the line between them? It seems easy to find parallels between romantic love, especially in its early stages, and addiction. There are cravings for close contact, heedless of risks, withdrawal symptoms from lost love, even relapse of a kind long after an affair is over.

And if we put on the neuroscientist's reductionist glasses, it is significant that the romantic phase of love activates the reward system's dopamine pathways in ways that resemble the response to addictive drugs. Magnetic resonance imaging (MRI) studies have shown enhanced activity in the nucleus accumbens –

◄▲ *I'll love you always – or at least until the dopamine hit wears off.*

that small region that is one of the main targets for neurons in the VTA – in lovers in relationships that have gone awry, and in those who are still happily coupled.

While at the Albert Einstein College of Medicine in New York Helen Fisher studied functional MRI (fMRI) responses of people in and out of love in detail. The matter-of-fact title of one of her most-read papers, from 2005, indicates her approach: "Romantic love: an fMRI study of a neural mechanism for mate choice".

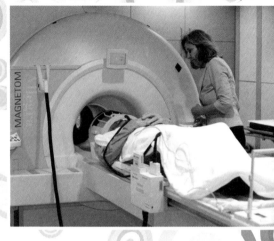

▲ Helen Fisher supervises an MRI scan.

Her point is that if love is a dopamine-mediated fixation – she calls it a "natural addiction" – that is for a good reason. Romantic love, in this view, is not an emotion (for all that emotion is part of the experience). It is a drive, part of a system that motivates us to achieve survival goals, in this case "a preferred mating partner".

There is a contrary view, that addiction should only be invoked in relation to love when it leads to bad outcomes – like compulsive seduction, or staying attached to a partner who is abusive or violent. However, a review of the research to date in 2017 by a group at the University of Oxford concluded that to be in love is to be "in some sense" addicted to another person. The main difference from other kinds of addiction would then be that a drug, or a pile of doughnuts, will never love you back.

ALTERED STATES

Drugs that boost dopamine have powerful attractions, but substances that alter perception in more diverse ways are at least as scientifically interesting.

Synthetic chemistry produced the first modern hallucinogen, LSD, in 1938, but its maker, Albert Hofmann, only discovered it was psychoactive by accident a few years later. We now know that its structure is a close match for the neurotransmitter serotonin – as are the active ingredients of hallucinogenic mushrooms and the American cactus-derived preparation, peyote. LSD is much more potent than those traditional bringers of visions, though, with a mere 25μG (micrograms) sufficient to alter consciousness.

▲ *Albert Hofmann.*

▼ *"Magic" mushroom spores seen under the electron microscope.*

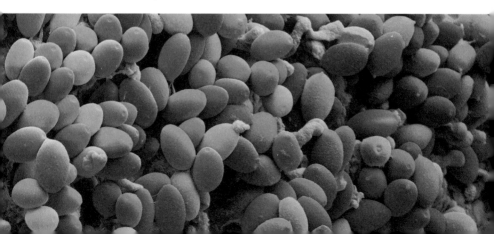

WHAT DO YOU SEE?

LSD and other psychedelics produce altered states of consciousness, everyone agrees. Saying what actually alters is harder, as consciousness remains a deep problem for neuroscience (see Chapter 11).

Research on LSD was proscribed for decades. A few brain-scanning studies have begun to portray its effects. It is very early days in this work, but there is recent evidence that areas not normally involved in visual processing help to generate what people see under the influence.

And a study published from the University of Sussex in 2017 suggested that some brain signals become more complex under the influence of three drugs: LSD, psilocybin (the active ingredient in "magic" mushrooms) and ketamine.

The study, widely reported as disclosing a "higher" state of consciousness, reanalysed data from several dozen volunteers who took drugs while rigged up with magnetoencephalography sensors. These give an indirect indication of neuronal activity by picking up minuscule magnetic changes induced by flows of ions in dendrites.

The new analysis applied an abstract mathematical measure of signal diversity, which is held to be a measure of the complexity of correlated brain activity. This is a very general index that can distinguish between signal patterns obtained from people who are awake or asleep, or in deep anaesthesia, so in that sense it may have something to do with consciousness. (The same method has been used to measure levels of consciousness more generally – see Chapter 11.)

On this measure, the drug-takers registered more than normal complexity. What does that mean? "The electrical activity of the brain is less predictable and less 'integrated' than during normal conscious wakefulness", according to Sussex researcher Anil Seth. It may be that LSD users already knew this.

TESTING, TESTING – ALEXANDER SHULGIN AND PSYCHEDELICS

Experimenting on human brains is not usually allowed, unless the brain is your own. The American researcher Alexander Shulgin, who died in 2014, developed his fascination with psychedelic drugs by synthesizing scores of new ones, and trying them out.

He left the Dow Chemical Company, where he had already synthesized the LSD-like amphetamine DOM, in the 1960s, but continued tinkering with molecular structures in a lab he built behind his house. For many years, the authorities allowed him to experiment freely, as long as he consulted for the Drug Enforcement Administration. He would make a new substance, estimate how much it might take to alter consciousness, then take a fraction of that dose, gradually increasing it until he felt the effects.

◀ *The chemical structure of MDMA, popularly known as ecstasy.*

Shulgin became famous in the late 1970s as the "godfather of ecstasy". He took MDMA (3,4-methylenedioxy-N-methylamphetamine) developed in a search for a blood-clotting agent, documented its effects on the brain, and published a new synthesis. When word got out, the drug found its way into nightclubs and raves around the world.

His licence to work with proscribed materials was withdrawn in the 1990s, but he carried on working on new compounds. He created more than 100 new psychoactive compounds during his career, many documented in his 1991 900-pager, *Phenethylamines I Have Known and Loved*, (known to aficionados as PiHKAL), and its sequel, *Tryptamines I Have Known and Loved* (or TiHKAL).

Shulgin was in favour of legalizing the drugs he tested, although as he told an interviewer in 2010, "usually they wait about four years after I get something out that becomes popular, and then they make it illegal."

He was a stickler for scientific rigour, and an advocate of the mind-expanding possibilities of psychedelics. His Shulgin Rating Scale for new compounds goes up to plus four, signifying reaching a new, transcendent state of consciousness. "If a drug (or technique or process) were ever to be discovered which would consistently produce a plus four experience in all human beings," he wrote, "it is conceivable that it would signal the ultimate evolution, and perhaps the end, of the human experiment."

▶ *Ecstasy for sale? MDMA pills.*

SHIFTING CURRENTS

Use of drugs to affect our brains is probably as old as our species. There were some early dalliances with electricity, but its uses as the main alternative method of manipulating brains are much more recent.

Many important discoveries have relied on direct stimulation of the brain with electrodes, but that only happens when someone needs urgent surgery. The most popular routes to altering electrical signals, by contrast, are noninvasive. The oldest that is adaptable for DIY users is light and sound stimulation. The electroencephalogram (EEG) pioneer Hans Berger discovered that EEG signals could be changed when subjects watched flickering lights. The bad news is that this can trigger fits; hence the warnings about strobe effects. But British physiologist Grey Walter reported in the 1950s that prolonged strobe exposure could induce hallucinations – leading some to try light machines as an alternative to psychedelic drugs, or as a way to enhance their effects. Commercial derivatives of such machines, using either light or sound, are still for sale on the internet, though there is little scientific evidence about the results of this kind of self-experimentation.

More obviously electrical is EEG-biofeedback, popularized in the 1970s. Simple devices for monitoring your own EEG – so that you can watch it in real time – also allow adepts to alter what is on a screen by concentrating on the waveform they want to see. The focus in the 1970s was on alpha waves, seen as a sign of relaxation akin to that achieved during meditation or yoga, or as a result of hypnosis. Later users have included other parts of the EEG trace in their efforts.

More recently, some clinical experiments have used fMRI as the monitor for biofeedback, which can help reduce chronic pain in some patients.

▶ The right kind of yoga can be a form of meditation, with similar effects on brain waves.

ZAPPING THE BRAIN

Attempts to apply electrical energy directly to the brain predate modern ideas about electricity, or brains. A Roman physician is said to have treated headaches and gout by applying the "torpedo fish" – although it's not clear which electric fish he used.

▲ *An unusually ornate early ECT apparatus.*

The first serious attempt to make use of electrical effects, though, did not happen until 1938, when Italian psychiatrist Ugo Cerletti applied electrodes to the temples of a patient with schizophrenia. It was intended to produce convulsions, which trials with chemicals had suggested could bring some relief from crushingly serious symptoms. In that sense, it was a move toward contemporary approaches because it assumed that the symptoms arise in the brain, so acting on the brain might be a viable alternative to psychotherapy.

The treatment caught on, and with the addition of anaesthetics and muscle relaxants was in widespread use by the mid-1940s, mainly for depression. The drugs meant the convulsions were confined to the brain. In effect, the patient had an artificially induced epileptic fit.

It is also the most controversial treatment in the history of psychiatry, justly so. That's partly because we still have little clue how it works – and applying a mains current to the temples does seem like trying to fix a radio by kicking it. But electroshock treatment was also used as a punishment in psychiatric hospitals in the 1950s. The famous scene in

which electroconvulsive therapy (ECT) is used to pacify an unruly patient, played by Jack Nicholson, in the 1975 film *One Flew Over the Cuckoo's Nest*, is "not completely unrealistic for the era it depicts" says medical historian Jonathan Sadowsky, choosing his words carefully.

Today, it is still used on perhaps a million people a year around the world. The carefully deployed modern version of ECT is used for some patients with crippling depression, and for some

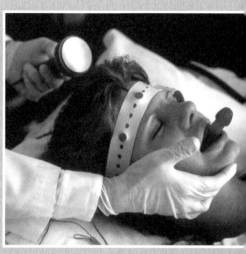

▼ Contemporary ECT is accompanied by anaesthetic.

others like severely autistic children who deliberately injure themselves. The anaesthetic and muscle relaxants make it outwardly uneventful. Still, it involves passing an electric current through the temporal lobes, seizures, and – often – memory loss. It does produce benefit for some patients when nothing else works, but it would be good if we understood why, and could produce the same effect in a more refined fashion.

◀ Catfish, rays and eels can all pack an electrical punch.

DEEP BRAIN STIMULATION

EEG, which picks up currents from the scalp, is less informative than recording electrical signals from electrodes inside the brain. In the same way, ECT is far less precise than direct electrical intervention via live electrodes. But when and where should they go, and what could they help?

The most impressive successes to date have involved Parkinson's disease. We know this is a degenerative disorder with loss of control over movements caused by death of dopamine producing cells in part of the midbrain, the substantia nigra.

There is no cure but efforts to relieve symptoms with dopamine precursors and related drugs have had some success. Deep brain stimulation (DBS) is an alternative when these lose their effect or produce unmanageable side effects. It is "deep" because this is not just applying electricity to the cortex, but reaching much further into the brain.

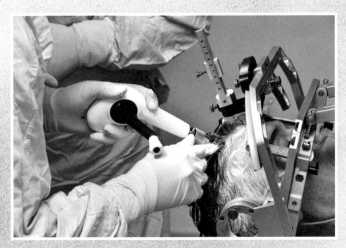

◀ Deep brain stimulation requires a surgically implanted electrode.

A small set of high-frequency electrodes have to be inserted inside the skull. As we do not really understand what the electricity is doing, the implant zone is chosen by a best guess from the individual symptoms, along with talking to the patient if the operation happens under a local anaesthetic.

Unlike ECT, the stimulation needs to be continuous. The electrodes are wired to a battery-powered unit, a bit like a heart pacemaker, that is usually implanted in the chest a day or two later, with wires running under the skin up to the brain. Unlike a pacemaker, the user can control it. The operation for Parkinson's patients has a 20-year history, and more than 100,000 people carry the implants.

▼ Schematic of deep brain electrodes wired to their powerpack. The electrodes are depicted larger than real life.

A BRIGHT FUTURE

DBS has one advantage over drug therapy – affecting a specific, small portion of the brain rather than the whole organ. Positive results with Parkinson's disease have encouraged experiments in treating some severe psychiatric disorders with DBS. The first targets are severe obsessive–compulsive disorder and depression which don't respond to other treatment. Results are slightly more promising so far for the former, but numbers are small in both cases. The problem with taking trials in these conditions further is deciding where to place the electrodes. Getting that right will probably depend on extracting reliable signatures of altered electrical activity in different conditions, using recording as well as stimulation on large groups of subjects. That is still some way off.

TRANSCRANIAL STIMULATION

DBS is deeply invasive, but other new techniques that can affect brains have a lighter touch. One is electrical, one magnetic – hence influencing electricity less directly. Their names are similar – transcranial direct current stimulation and transcranial magnetic stimulation – because they both rely on devices outside the skull.

DIRECT CURRENT STIMULATION

The electrical variety is a little like ECT-lite. It involves activating electrodes that pass a small current, measured in milliamps. It is strong enough to feel when switched on, but doesn't make neurons fire directly. One theory is that it affects the probability of firing by altering membrane potentials.

As it is easy to do and relatively innocuous, it has been tried for all manner of medical conditions – from depression to schizophrenia to chronic pain – as well as in hopes of improving learning, memory or even intelligence. Randomized trials have hardly begun, and those published so far show little demonstrable benefit. Beyond the clinic, you can do it yourself with a kit bought off the internet, although I won't be trying it at home.

▲ *Direct Current Stimulation.*
◀ *Magnetic Stimulation.*

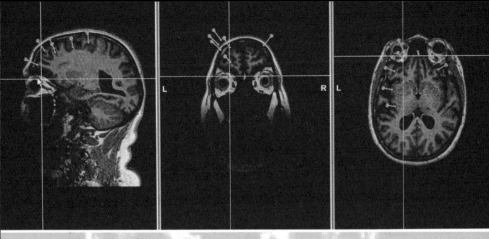

▲ *An MRI scan is used to help identify the best regions of the cortex to target for magnetic stimulation that might relieve symptoms of depression.*

MAGNETIC STIMULATION

Magnetic stimulation is simpler still, involving an electromagnetic coil near the skull that delivers a brief magnetic pulse. Such pulses produce electric fields inside the brain – the tissue effectively acting as the secondary coil you would find in a laboratory demonstration of induction. This can affect neurons, but the field decays rapidly with distance so only influences a depth of brain of a couple of centimetres (about an inch). It is also harder to localize than transcranial electrical stimulation.

Single-shot magnetic stimulation is used diagnostically, especially to assess damage in stroke patients. The technique also has research uses, but wider interest has again focused on possible therapeutic benefits. Repeated magnetic stimulation has been tried for severe depression and chronic pain. Commercial kits tend to be aimed at migraine sufferers, where single pulse magnetic stimulation does seem to produce relief from attacks.

As this still involves dealing with a condition whose cause is not known with a treatment that isn't fully understood, it may be best to regard magnetic stimulation as largely a research technique for now. The current state of the art in brain manipulation suggests that asking, "can I see you do it first?" is a good rule to follow when a new method is on offer.

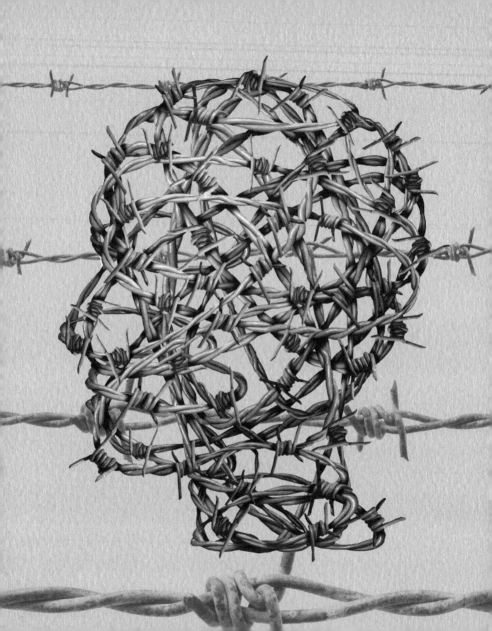

CHAPTER 10

BRAINS IN DISTRESS

THE DIAGNOSTIC CHALLENGE

> *"Canst thou not minister to a mind diseased, pluck from the memory a rooted sorrow, raze out the written troubles of the brain and with some sweet oblivious antidote cleanse the stuff'd bosom of that perilous stuff that weighs upon the heart?"*

Shakespeare's words, voiced by Macbeth, have a modern ring. But even though we recognize that distressed brains cause human suffering, useful understanding remains elusive. Research has revealed much about the workings of brains. Yet clinical approaches to mental health have only a nodding acquaintance with contemporary neuroscience, which mainly offers hope for the future.

Investigation of brains at the level of cells and synapses has been immensely fruitful, but remains hard to relate to high-level phenomena like moods, altered perceptions and behaviour, and states of consciousness. Those are what we are trying to reach in psychiatric illness, and doing that is still largely reliant on the best guesses of thoughtful doctors rather than anything more scientific.

Neuroscience has made a difference in clarifying how chemical treatments for some conditions affect neurons. That clarification, mostly involving neurotransmitters, has made administering some drugs – whose effects were often discovered by accident – easier to justify, and helped improve others. But it does not yet amount to a complete account of why they help.

DEFINING NORMAL

The disconnect I've described is especially clear in diagnosis. The *Diagnostic and Statistical Manual of Mental Disorders* of the American Psychiatric Association, now in its fifth edition, runs to 1,000 pages covering over 150 different conditions. It's an impressive inventory of symptoms. But diagnosis is guided mainly by checklists, not by anything detected directly in the brain. Most conditions are defined by the way people behave, or say they feel. There are few other measurable markers. Moreover, for any given symptom there are usually some people without it who still get diagnosed, and some who have the symptom, but not the condition. After a century or more of scientific psychiatry, mental illness or disability is still often highly negotiable. And recent debates about some diagnoses indicate that how that negotiation goes sometimes depends on what counts as normal functioning, and how everyone else deals with difference.

▼ *Treatment of mental illness has improved immeasurably since Hogarth painted Bedlam in eighteenth-century London, but diagnosis is still problematic.*

FROM SERENDIPITY TO SEROTONIN

In 1952, experimental use of a drug on patients with tuberculosis in the USA had an unexpected result. The drug, a candidate antihistamine known as iproniazid, did not do much for their illness. But the previously deeply downcast patients became light-hearted, even exuberant.

Later work showed that the drug inhibited an enzyme, monoamine oxidase, which breaks down several simple molecules that act as neurotransmitters, including dopamine and serotonin. By the end of the decade, it was being marketed as an antidepressant. Improved drugs in the same class, the monoamine oxidase inhibitors (MAOIs), were widely used through the 1960s and 1970s. Their advent marked what the UK psychiatrist David Healy calls the antidepressant era.

It was significant in several ways. A drug that acted on levels of neurotransmitters (increasing their availability in this case) seemed to offer a scientific way of treating the brain. Chemical therapy helped to convince doctors and patients of the assumption we now take for granted – that psychiatric conditions have

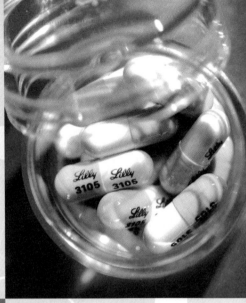

▶ Drugs for major mental illnesses are a mainstay of the modern pharmaceutical industry.

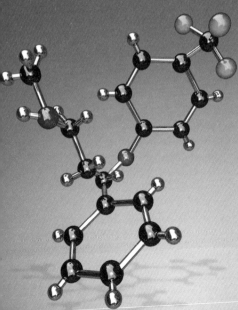

biological underpinnings. And it gave direction to a mass of further research on causes, and consequences, of psychiatric conditions, and how they might be treated.

The treatments tend to run ahead of the science. Hefty promotion by drug companies can encourage that. But serious psychiatric illness is debilitating, sometimes life-threatening. Treating it is too urgent to wait for complete scientific

◀ Fluoxetine, which increases serotonin levels, came into use as an antidepressant in the 1980s.

understanding of what's happening. So doctors' efforts to help patients develop in a to-and-fro with researchers theorizing about why particular things might work. The history of psychiatric drugs is a tangle of chance findings, and of plausible ideas about the action of psychopharmaceuticals that led to improvements even though the ideas later turned out to be of limited use, or wrong.

Serotonin looms large in the story, but its significance has shifted and shimmered as different lines of research have unfolded. The later generation of antidepressants, the selective serotonin reuptake inhibitors (SSRIs), increase availability of this particular neurotransmitter by blocking the transporters that remove it from the

synaptic cleft. This avoids a mixture of effects (and side effects) from the MAOI's action on levels of several different neurotransmitters. The early SSRIs, such as Prozac, introduced in 1987, produced spectacular benefits in some deeply ill patients. Serotonin appeared to some like the key to contentment. It seemed Prozac might even be a drug anyone could take to feel "better than well".

Convincing neuroscience theory to back up the idea was hard to come by, though, and efforts to clarify serotonin's role were confounded by a mass of contradictory results. For one thing, SSRIs are only selective in one sense – they affect just the one neurotransmitter. But the single molecule has many effects, produced via at least seven different families of receptors, and many receptor subtypes.

A further challenge is to explain why symptom relief in depression normally does not happen for several weeks, when neurotransmitters, and their transporters, are involved in very rapid events at the molecular level.

The same is true when SSRIs are used to treat anxiety disorders. These conditions, which include panic attacks, phobias, post-traumatic stress disorder and obsessive-compulsive

disorder (OCD), may respond to benzodiazepine tranquillizers, when there is no delay. It turned out that SSRIs helped some people, too, but with these drugs the same lag was seen as when they were used to treat depression. Benzodiazepines enhance the effects of gamma-amino-butyric-acid (GABA), the inhibitory neurotransmitter, so a rapid damping down effect makes sense. But the action of the SSRIs is harder to fathom.

◀ *A preoccupation with cleanliness is often one of the symptoms of obsessive compulsive disorder.*

▼ *An artist's impression of an inhibitory drug blocking re-uptake of serotonin after it is released from the synapse (top).*

ANXIETY IN THE DNA

Further work on anxiety disorders and serotonin illustrates some of the complexities of multiple causation and subtle variations in effects that neuroscience tends to reveal when researchers probe the details of particular medical conditions.

The overall framework in which anxiety is theorized is the current understanding of the brain's response to stress. This involves a cascade of hormones, beginning with corticotropin-releasing hormone, which is made by specialized neurons in the hypothalamus. Its message is received by the pituitary gland, which then releases adrenocorticotropic hormone. That in turn stimulates the adrenal gland on top of the kidneys to release the steroid hormone, cortisol. This final molecule has a host of physiological effects related to stress and response to threats. But they all begin in the brain. The initial neuronal secretion is regulated by brain circuits that have been identified in the amygdala and the hippocampus – the latter itself responding to cortisol in one of several feedback loops.

◀ Anxiety disorders may run in families, lending weight to theories that they are affected by alterations in genes involved in transport of neurotransmitters.

How, then, does serotonin fit into this apparently well-understood system? That part is not so clear. At one time, the fact that anxiety disorders tend to run in families aligned well with studies of mutations in serotonin transporter genes. In the early noughties, patients from two different families with a high incidence of one form of OCD were found to have a pair of gene mutations. Both of them made the transporter more active. If you recall, it is involved in reuptake of the neurotransmitter after it is released at a synapse, which means this crucial chemical messenger is less active in these people.

This remains one of the strongest links found between relatively simple genetic changes and behaviour, but affecting just a few people. However, we now know that this kind of change is not just passed down from parent to child. There are other alterations in DNA apart from inherited mutations in the sequence, known as *epigenetic* changes. These usually involve modifying one of the chemical units in the DNA chain by adding a small additional unit, a methyl group. Such additions affect whether enzymes can latch on to the DNA strand and thus help regulate gene activity.

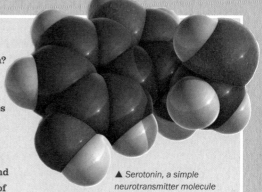

▲ Serotonin, a simple neurotransmitter molecule that stimulates many different receptors in the brain.

In 2014, a group at Duke University recorded small differences in methylation of the serotonin transporter gene in saliva collected from a group of 80 college students. And increased methylation went with "increased threat-related amygdala activity" when the same people were scanned while looking at fearful or angry faces.

In this case, the slightly altered gene *decreased* transporter activity, just one aspect of this study that raises additional questions. But the demonstration that epigenetic changes, a kind of annotation of the genes that is usually considered a response to environmental influences in the individual's life, can be linked to effects in the brain emphasizes how many variables can influence the way parts of the brain are organized.

DIRECT ACTION FOR DEPRESSION?

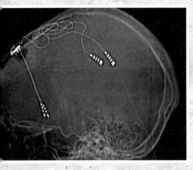

▲ *An X-ray shows electrodes inserted for deep brain stimulation.*

Drugs and talking therapy may help people with depression without a full account of how they work. In very serious cases, electroshock treatment is still in use (see Chapter 9). But can neuroscience help to target depression more directly?

There are hints that this may be possible. Since the 1990s, imaging studies have tried to build a picture of differences in brain activity among depressed subjects. Progress has been slow. As with scanning findings in general, many studies have been small, reducing their reliability and often yielding results that others fail to repeat. In depression, the largest meta-analysis so far – smooshing together data from many studies to give a statistically more robust result – found no differences on average between activity scans of depressed subjects and everyone else.

However, like the other general psychiatric categories, depression probably labels a set of distinct paths brains can follow, with different starting and finishing points. And accumulating evidence from scans has persuaded some researchers there are useful subdivisions of activity patterns that go with different clusters of symptoms.

In the early 2000s, Helen Mayberg of Emory University in the USA suggested that positron emission tomography and

▲ Precise targeting of stimulation on four specific nerve tracts in the brain may help some patients with depression.

functional magnetic resonance imaging pointed to an area of the cortex – the subcallosal cingulate region, also known as Brodmann area 25 – that played a crucial role in a "depression circuit". It appears to change in similar ways when depression treatments work, but resists change in patients who show no improvement in their symptoms.

That prompted efforts to target this area for treatment in people who were severely depressed and didn't respond to existing therapy. The logic was similar to the use of electroconvulsive therapy, but something more refined was called for, so experiments began with deep brain stimulation using implanted electrodes in this region.

Early results appeared to show improvement in some intractably depressed patients. A first clinical trial of the implant for depression was halted in 2013, amid conflicting reports of the reasons, but the work at Emory continues.

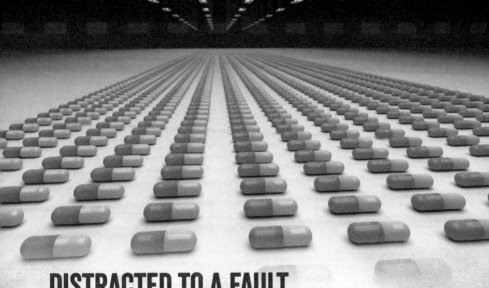

DISTRACTED TO A FAULT

Our senses are evolved to highlight differences, and our attention will jump when a novel stimulus appears – perhaps to prepare us for fight or flight. But we also have to concentrate for long stretches to do lots of the complicated things that make us human. Anyone who aspires to the latter – to write a book, perhaps – sometimes struggles with the balance between attention and distraction. But constantly losing the fight against distraction is classified as a medical problem.

Attention deficit hyperactivity disorder (ADHD) is probably the most controversial condition in psychiatry. It is simultaneously widely diagnosed and subject to claims that, notwithstanding its entry in all the official classifications, it does not really exist.

More and more schoolchildren have been diagnosed with ADHD in the last few decades, especially in the USA where the incidence in some places is almost 10 per cent. And many of those children have been treated with the stimulant drugs methylphenidate (Ritalin) or amphetamine, as well as non-drug therapy. Some see this as a sign of an alarming intolerance of disorderly behaviour, others as a welcome indication that children who used to get no help coping with social expectations and demands are now having their needs taken seriously.

The controversy endures partly because ADHD, like other psychiatric conditions, is diagnosed from a behavioural checklist, rather than any more objective test. The behaviour is different in degree, not kind, from everyone else's, and diagnosis is a matter of judgement. It is easy to see that people with severe attention problems need help. But how far along into the mid-range should treatment go – and what are the costs of long-term drug dosage?

Neuroscience's role here, as usual, is to strive for clarity about what might underlie the condition, how to treat it if necessary, and how the treatments work.

▼ *Children's susceptibility to distraction is part of their charm. So when does it become a problem?*

Much of the relevant research has centred on dopamine. The drugs used appear to help. We know they act on neurotransmission, increasing dopamine levels in synapses. But it proved difficult to establish consistent results about dopamine levels, or dopamine transporter activity, in ADHD patients. Suggestions that dopamine receptors in key brain regions might be thin on the ground were also hard to confirm.

More recent studies have focused attention (as it were) on parts of the prefrontal cortex, which may have less grey matter in ADHD subjects. There is also evidence that methylphenidate increases otherwise low dopamine levels, in a region deeper in the cerebral hemispheres known as the caudate, in test subjects who performed poorly on attention-intensive tasks. That result held for both ADHD patients *and* a control group, though, making it harder to argue for a simple dopamine-shortage-causes-ADHD link.

As in other areas of mental health, there are many other results, from brain scans, from studies implicating effects of other neurotransmitters in

▼ *Image from a study using PET scanning to investigate dopamine levels in ADHD.*

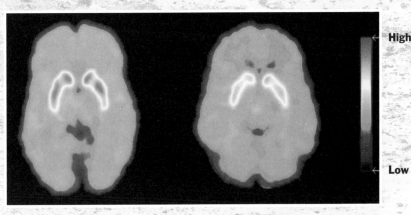

High

Low

Control subject　　　**ADHD subject**

particular regions, and findings of gene variations, that influence the chances of developing severe ADHD. As all these lines of investigation develop, it is likely to emerge as another disorder where a complex of causes, in different combinations, produces differences in brain development that manifest in superficially similar ways. Meanwhile, other researchers are refining the comparison between drug treatment and other ways of helping children and adolescents with ADHD, and assessing the effects of longer-term drug administration, as well as how children treated for ADHD fare as adults.

▲ One-to-one therapy with an adult is an alternative approach to ADHD.

DIFFERENCE, DEFICITS AND DIVERSITY

When does a difference become a disorder? If the condition in question is in the brain, the people exhibiting the difference may have an opinion about that.

The recent history of autism illustrates how the question can be as much a social and political one as a guide for biomedical research. Autism was long defined as a severe developmental and behavioural disorder, disrupting language use and social interaction. It is strongly heritable, though not simply – many genes are implicated. Other influences matter, too, and as with ADHD it is likely that multiple possible causes can lead to superficially similar outcomes. Neuroscience has thrown up many possibilities for how important features of autism relate to brain development and activity, such as

◀ Part of an assessment that can help diagnose autism.

▲ Temple Grandin meets her public, but her work rests on an unusual affinity for animals.

differences in brain scans when people see faces, or listen to spoken language. Some still hope for a cure for what in the worst cases can be a profoundly disabling condition.

At the same time, it is now recognized that those cases lie at one end of a broad spectrum, and as Steve Silberman relates in his history *NeuroTribes*, autism and Asperger's syndrome, once regarded as distinct conditions, have now been incorporated into the portmanteau autism spectrum disorder (ASD).

The spectrum includes people whose difficulties are relatively slight, as well as high-functioning autistics who learn to cope with social interactions that other people deal with automatically. This, along with the realization that some behavioural traits associated with autism are relatively widespread, has led autism activists to propose that ASD, diverse as it is, is itself an example of neurodiversity.

The suggestion is that brains are similar overall but may develop along different trajectories. An individual can become neurotypical, or end up with one of a number of distinct neural formations – which may not necessarily be a problem. People with some autistic traits need special consideration, especially allowing them to avoid social or sensory overload, but then manage perfectly well. Some develop particular talents, like the autistic scientist Temple Grandin, an expert on livestock behaviour who ascribes her insights to being more attuned to visual thinking than other people.

Schizophrenia, on the other hand, is a destructive disorder that often disrupts lives permanently. Nonetheless, some common symptoms – such as hearing voices – are things that brains and minds encounter more widely.

There are two general scientific arguments that may favour neurodiversity. There may be evolutionary advantage in maintaining a range of different abilities across a population of brains. And the view that much of the brain is organized in a modular way allows that different modules may be more or less developed in different people.

One task for future neuroscience is to investigate more deeply how broad the range of human types may be – a problem that until now has been mainly pondered by psychologists, whose inventories of personality types are still fairly restricted, and novelists.

Lives like hers offer powerful support for the general notion that a difference does not mean a defect. This has helped encourage others to take the notion of neurodiversity further, with claims that ADHD, dyslexia, Tourette syndrome, and even schizophrenia, are examples of variations in the brain.

Is this over-extending a useful idea? In ADHD there is already controversy about the incidence of a condition whose diagnosis appears to depend on doing things that nearly everyone does, but much more of the time.

HEARING VOICES

In 1987, Dutch psychiatrist Marius Romme asked television viewers to write in if they had ever heard voices, a diagnostic criterion for schizophrenia. He heard from 700 people who described self-generated auditory input, and was surprised to learn that 500 of them had no problem dealing with it, and had never been psychiatric patients.

He felt that voices were usually meaningful, and that people who received disturbing messages had often started hearing them after some traumatic experience, such as childhood abuse or the death of a close relative. This idea, along with evidence from other cultures where hearing voices is treated as less of an aberration than it is in the modern West, led to the establishment of the Hearing Voices Network. Groups the network organizes, in 30 countries, encourage people to talk about voices they hear, and what they say, without any suggestion they are ill.

Their work is not a substitute for medical care for people who are seriously ill, but can offer coping strategies – such as negotiating with voices that give orders – for people who experience this particular difference from neurotypical life.

DEALING WITH DEMENTIA

The casual phrase "losing your mind" can become a brutal reality when the brain begins to falter because its tissues are damaged. Degeneration that leads to dementia, usually irreversible, often progressive, can result from a variety of causes – including the genetic condition Huntington's disease, and multiple tiny strokes.

The most common cause, Alzheimer's disease, offers a contrast with psychiatric conditions, as it can be diagnosed from unambiguous biological signs – though not usually while the patient lives. From the neuroscientific perspective, it is an increasingly urgent test case. Can a more detailed dissection of changes in brain tissue help prevent, delay or alleviate symptoms – losing memory, confusion, and sometimes drastic personality changes – that affect more and more people in an ageing population? In the USA, for example, current projections suggest there will be 14 million people with Alzheimer's disease by 2020.

Despite all our new insights into the brain, the payoff in this case has yet to appear. The cause, as far as we can tell, is not subtle. Tangles of a small protein

◀ *Ageing may lead to a frightening loss of identity in some cases.*

(beta-amyloid plaques) accumulate between neurons, while others (made of a protein called tau) appear inside them. Neurons die, and the brain shrinks. There are other, subtler, changes, but the aberrant clumps of protein are probably at the root of the disease. The best guess is that they arise when a protein assumes an unusual form, one that alters its interactions with other protein molecules. They get tangled up, and resist cells' regular garbage disposal. Similar things are seen in late stage Huntington's disease and the prion-protein diseases Creutzfeldt-Jakob disease and bovine spongiform encephalopathy ("mad cow disease").

The idea also fits with one of the several known gene variants that affects the risk of Alzheimer's. Alterations in the amyloid precursor protein (APP)

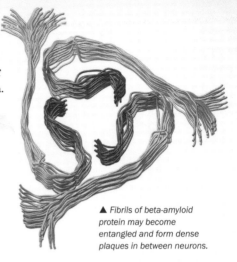

▲ *Fibrils of beta-amyloid protein may become entangled and form dense plaques in between neurons.*

gene can lead to early onset Alzheimer's presumably because they make the altered protein form more likely, or more stable.

The main goal of research is to find ways to clear away the protein junk that causes the damage. We don't know how to do that yet. In the meantime, anti-Alzheimer's drugs increase levels of neurotransmitters, so remaining neurons communicate more efficiently, but have only modest effects and only for a short while.

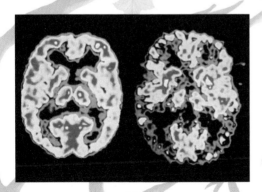

◀ *Scan of a normal brain (left), and one showing tissue loss in late stage Alzheimer's disease.*

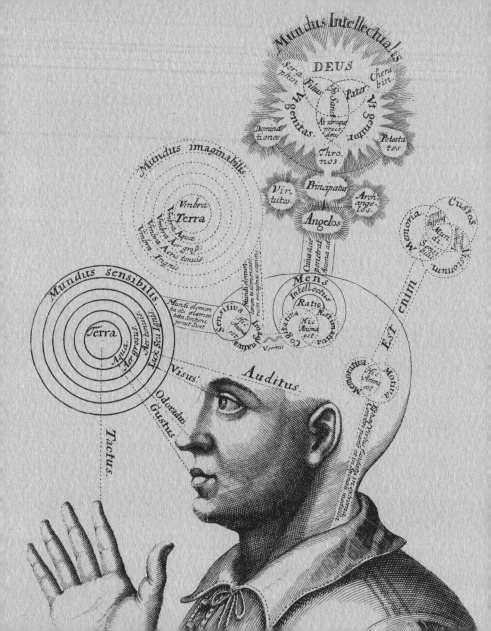

CHAPTER 11

SELFIE SCIENCE

KNOW THYSELF

Wanting to know ourselves better is a powerful driver for neuroscience. Part of our sense of self comes from embodiment, but it is held together by the brain. Consider organ transplants. The recipient normally benefits. But a brain transplant? You definitely want to be the donor.

But how is it that each of us feels he or she is a person, with a history and an identity that span a lifetime? Neuroscience agrees with Freud that much of what makes the self is unconscious. The brain has no need to make us aware of most of what it does. Indeed, consciousness – a sort of icing on the neural cake – used not to be a respectable scientific topic. Most assumed that it arises from neural events, but there was plenty of work to get on with without intruding on philosophers' turf by speculating about how some brains became conscious.

That has changed. Researchers are now interested in the neural correlates of consciousness as well as unconscious processes. That interest covers basic

▲ *Sigmund Freud emphasized that much of what our minds do is unconscious.*

state differences, like being awake or asleep, and the mechanisms of attention and awareness. It extends to locating brain regions involved in generating the sense of an integrated, conscious self making its way in the world, and the associated unfolding narrative, that most of us seem to possess.

The research is rich, and has revealed ways consciousness can be manipulated. How close are we to understanding the origins of consciousness, or how the sense of a unified self is maintained? That is still energetically debated.

THE CARTESIAN THEATRE

Philosopher Daniel Dennett has strong views about how the brain *doesn't* work. In his ambitiously titled book *Consciousness Explained* he says that many accounts of consciousness assume that there is a kind of virtual projection screen in the brain – and perceptions that appear there in sequence add up to our flow of conscious awareness. The obvious flaw in this picture, he points out, is that there is no one to look at the screen.

He calls this idea the Cartesian theatre to imply it is a carry-over from Descartes' dualist separation of mind from brain in the 17th century.

▲ *Daniel Dennett.*

the seat of consciousness?

PAY ATTENTION!

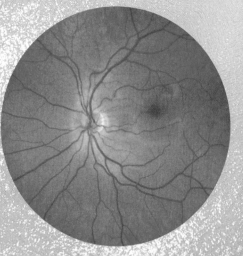

▼ *Visual receptors cover the retina, but are most densely packed in the centre.*

Being conscious of something, in the simple sense of awareness, first calls for picking it out from the barrage of information reaching the senses. It is the antidote to what William James famously dubbed the "blooming, buzzing confusion" of the world.

The mechanisms of attention have been intensively studied, mainly in the visual system. Ingenious psychological experiments, combined with electrical recordings from key brain regions, have established some important features of how it works.

The eye quickly aligns the small, central patch of the retina, the fovea – where close-packed cells allow the most acute vision – with an item of interest. Although our eyes are making constant small movements, saccades, we can also move them deliberately. If you concentrate on the details of any personal encounter, you'll be reminded that we read a lot into where someone is directing their gaze.

But there is another component of visual attention, which is separate from eye movements. In the 1970s and 1980s, experiments confirmed that the brain has a "spotlight" that directs attention to a particular small portion of the visual field, and is *not* tied to where the fovea is pointing. It's actually a slightly misleading metaphor, as it implies a beam highlighting detail, rather than a selection from incoming information, but it caught on with researchers nonetheless.

In a typical experiment, people are faster – by around 50 milliseconds – in pushing a button when they see a light if it was preceded by a visual clue, as simple as an arrow, of where it was going to appear.

The trick is to show the clue so close to the appearance of the light that there is no time for the eye to move. Somehow, attention shifts, or at least begins to, while the eye remains stationary. It is hard to explain how this can happen without the brain doing the job as it processes changing visual input.

Although this is only one aspect of attention, it explains how we can watch something, or someone "out of the corner of our eye". We are moving the metaphorical spotlight while keeping our gaze directed elsewhere, so our observation is disguised.

▶ Attending to the right information moment to moment promotes survival in fast-changing environments.

PUTTING REALITY TOGETHER

Visual attention studies remind us that the brain is organized to break down the world, as sensory information, into many smaller pieces, and work on them separately. The visual system then needs to reassemble an overall picture of what is in front of the viewer – a process that is still not well understood (see Chapter 5).

In the same way, whatever is responsible for consciousness needs to piece together an overall sense of the situation a brain's owner finds themselves in. In vision, this is known as the binding problem, and it takes on new dimensions when we need to integrate representations from many different processes.

The visual system offers the brain's construct of a scene, rather than showing

what's "really" out there. Similarly, our consciousness is filled with judicious edits, exuberant joining of dots, and hypotheses disguised as strong inferences. We do not know exactly how this all works, but there is plenty of evidence that it happens.

Take two examples at differing levels of sophistication. Visual attention is closely linked to the constant, rapid movements that our eyes make – around three times a second, 150,000 times a day. Yet we can watch objects in motion wholly unconscious of the tracking mechanism directing the eye, (or read a line of text like this one blithely ignoring the way the eye skips along it). The brain simultaneously directs the movements, some of the fastest muscle actions in the body, and screens them from awareness.

◀ *We feel we "take in a scene" at a glance, but the brain takes it apart, then reassembles it.*

THE CAPGRAS DELUSION

A more vivid indication that consciousness is part fabrication is the rare psychosis, Capgras delusion, in which people fail to recognize a relative, or friend (or perhaps a pet). This goes beyond simple visual recognition, which fails for faces in prosopagnosia. People with Capgras syndrome experience a familiar face, unaccompanied by the emotional response they have been used to – perhaps because of a neurodegenerative condition.

▼ *Sometimes a robot really is a robot.*

This separation of two inputs that normally go together might just leave someone puzzled or distressed. But the response is stronger. Capgras delusion typically involves insistence that the person concerned is an imposter, perhaps even a robot, who has been substituted for the real significant other. The brain, confronted with otherwise baffling information, makes up a story, which then becomes an unshakeable conscious belief.

TO SLEEP, PERCHANCE TO DREAM

Sleep is neuroscientifically fascinating as so much normal activity is suspended. It is an essential part of the brain's routine. We don't really know why, but current theorizing holds this is partly because it helps memory consolidation.

Meanwhile, it also allows some studies of consciousness. We have dream experiences while we sleep. And they are conjured up inside the brain, while sensory inputs are damped down.

Most people have heard of rapid eye movement (REM) sleep, when vivid dreams happen (though dreams can also occur in non-REM sleep). Electroencephalogram (EEG) traces in these phases of sleep resemble those of people who are awake.

Dreaming can be studied by waking people up after taking their EEG and asking them whether they were dreaming. In this way, experimenters find that dream states go with activation of a portion of the posterior cortex, inferred from a change from slow brain waves to faster cycles. The results can be tested by predicting when people were dreaming from their EEG read-outs.

When people are asked about the content of their dreams, EEG changes

▼ *This subject is asleep, but the EEG shows his brain is far from inactive.*

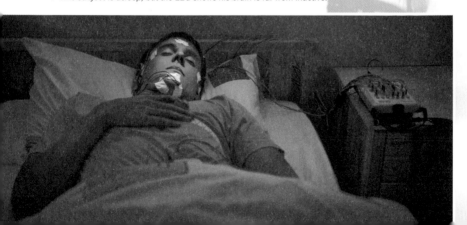

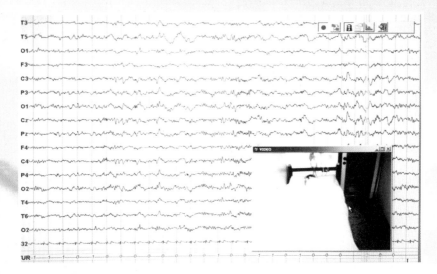

▲ *Following EEG traces can predict when a sleeper is dreaming, and even yield information about the kind of dream they are having.*

in particular brain regions correlated with dream features, such as seeing faces, experiencing motion, or hearing voices. The traces are the same as those expected if the subjects had been awake having similar experiences.

These recent findings are a moderately good fit with a theory proposed by sleep specialist Allan Hobson of Harvard University. He suggests that dreaming is a "protoconscious" state: when the brain dreams, it conjures up a virtual reality model of the world. Hobson sees this as a kind of dry run for consciousness. The dreaming brain rehearses the integration of systems that full consciousness relies on. But it uses self-generated inputs instead of taking on the full burden of sensory processing and memory retrieval that attend waking life.

There is a lot more detail in Hobson's theory, but his core proposition is that waking consciousness and brain activation occurring during sleep are closely related.

CONSCIOUS: HOW MUCH?

▲ Giulio Tononi.

If consciousness is a thing, science wants to measure it.
One way of doing so looks as if it works, as far as it goes.

The perturbational complexity index is in part a test of a broad theory of consciousness proposed by Giulio Tononi of the University of Wisconsin–Madison. He suggests that consciousness arises when information is shared between many different parts of the brain, and might be measured by assessing how much information is being integrated across brain regions.

A team at the University of Milan took him up on it in 2013. They used a short burst of transcranial magnetic stimulation to give neural processing a kick, then recorded activity all over the brain in the next 300 milliseconds via 60 EEG channels.

Processing and analysing the signals followed a complicated procedure to derive an index they defined as "the normalized Lempel-Ziv complexity of the spatiotemporal pattern of cortical activation".

The rest of us can assess its significance by following how it varied. In a series of experiments, it could reliably distinguish between subjects who were awake, asleep while dreaming, deeply asleep, or sedated by progressively stronger anaesthetics. And these states were ordered by the index as you would expect, from highest to lowest. The most alert subject scored 0.67 on their index, with the lowest index among the wakeful reading out at 0.44. In the deeply anaesthetized, it fell into the 0.1–0.3 range. Separate studies suggest it is increased above normal under the influence of LSD (see Chapter 9).

This does suggest that, however indirectly, this mathematically sophisticated but still rough and ready method is measuring something significant that relates to consciousness.

As well as its theoretical interest, the index can help in assessing people who have been in a coma. The same technique registered patients who were so injured they remained in a vegetative state at the same level as unconscious subjects. However, a pair of post-coma patients with locked-in syndrome, which is notoriously hard to detect, produced index readings of 0.5 and 0.6, a strong indicator that they were aware but unable to communicate.

◀ Multi-channel EEG is recorded from this cosy cap of electrodes.

THE HARD PROBLEM

Tracking patterns of activity in neurons yields clues about which parts of the brain contribute to consciousness. Exactly how is not yet clear – and not everyone believes this is the right path to explore. The physicist Roger Penrose, for example, proposes that consciousness – and free will – depend on components of neurons, perhaps the complex weave of proteins in microtubules, influenced by quantum mechanical effects. He has few supporters among active researchers, though, who focus on the kinds of neural activity that feature throughout this book.

▲ Sir Roger Penrose.

They generally admit, though, that a crucial aspect of consciousness remains beyond the reach of their experiments. It is most often described as the hard problem, a term coined by philosopher David Chalmers in 1995. Suppose you piece together a complete account of neurons signalling when someone looks at a wall painted bright red. Include all the associated work of attention, visual processing,

▼ Microtubules provide scaffolding and transport links inside cells. But could they be tied in to consciousness as well?

▶ Seeing red is familiar to most. But how do we convey that experience to someone who is colour blind?

reintegration, and awareness of the result. That, said Chalmers, counts as the (relatively) easy problem, or problems, which might be soluble in principle. But it still would not tell you what it feels like to see red if you are colour blind.

This seems the most puzzling feature of conscious experience: you cannot tell someone how it was for you unless they already know what it is like. The sensory elements that make up an experience – seeing red remains everyone's favourite example – are termed "qualia". These fundamentals of sensation are a thing in themselves. Think of wine tasting notes. Every

nuance of the finest vintage is compared to the taste or smell of something else. The language is shared, but the system of reference circular.

Some philosophers deny that the hard problem is crucial, and believe consciousness will be explained one day by ignoring it. I think the preoccupation with simple sensations makes it too easy. I recall an eminent mathematician I interviewed describing how he worked. When he was trying hard, he said, he would address his problem by *holding it in his mind* all day. I get the words, but if I try and relate this to my own, much less rich, experience of mathematics, I don't have much idea what he meant.

WE KNOW YOU KNOW

There is a second hard problem concerning consciousness: why and how did human self-consciousness evolve?

Archaeologist Steven Mithen argued in *The Prehistory of the Mind* in the 1990s that the traces left by protohumans show little sign that they could combine different cognitive abilities – for fashioning tools, recognizing other species in their ecosystem, or navigating social life. Consciousness, for Mithen, allows that read-across between domains. He agrees with the British psychologist Nicholas Humphrey and anthropologist Robin Dunbar that our kind of self-consciousness

probably emerged to help deal with the complexities of life in ever larger groups.

We know our own minds, Humphrey suggested, because that allows us to imagine what might be in the minds of others – a trick other creatures cannot manage. That allows us to predict other people's behaviour, and cope with the complexities of inter-group relations. The same line of thinking, developed by Dunbar, suggests that the first benefit of language was to extend the

◀ *Robin Dunbar.*

▶ *Nicholas Humphrey.*

▲ *Gossip is fundamental to human social life, and to fathoming others' intentions.*

strengthening of close ties between individuals that is achieved in other primates by grooming. Words allowed us to "groom" more people, via gossip, and hence keep track of a larger band of acquaintances.

They also transform thinking in other ways. The key idea here is what philosophers call intentionality. If I know (or think I know) that you know something, that involves one level of intentionality. Chimpanzees can manage that, and there is evidence they can sometimes stretch to a second level. But some time since we parted company with the common ancestor we share with the chimp we evolved brains that can go much further. Wide-awake humans can keep track of five orders of intentionality, on a good day, though six are usually too confusing. When we try and puzzle over something like: "If they think we think they know this, then we think they will imagine us doing that", we are in danger of overloading our mind's capacity for keeping track of intentionality, however it is managed inside a nest of neurons.

OTHER MINDS

Other people can deceive us, or just seem confusing. But we can get *some* idea what it is like to be someone else when they put thoughts and feelings into words. What do other creatures have in mind, though?

The question would only occur to a person. Dogs, I reckon, don't worry about what it is like to be a cat, or a human. We can imagine some features of a dog's life. Their attentiveness to smell must give a streetscape or park a very different set of markers to the ones we notice, we who rely more on vision. Their qualia will be different.

Some creatures are more different still. What, asked the philosopher Thomas Nagel in a famous paper, is it like to be a bat? Their information about the world comes from echolocation. They can analyse complex ultrasound echoes fast enough to catch insects on the wing in a cave thick with other bats. Hard to relate that to anything we can sense. As Nagel put it, "anyone who has spent some time in an enclosed space with an excited bat knows what it is to encounter a fundamentally *alien* form of life."

We can go further away from home base, neurologically speaking. A bat, after all, is still a mammal. Consider the octopus. They are pretty intelligent, and people who have close encounters report exchanging glances, even touch, with an entity that knows they are there – as philosopher and scuba diver

Peter Godfrey-Smith relates in his book *Other Minds*.

But octopus minds, if that is the word, are nothing like ours. The last common ancestor of the cephalopods (octopus, squid and cuttlefish) and other creatures with complex nervous systems lived 600 million years ago. An octopus can have 500-million-odd neurons, but most of them are in the arms, which are equipped with taste and smell sensors as well as touch.

It lives in a world in which it is natural to have eight legs, blue-green blood, and pigment cells in your skin that can change colour in an eye-blink. Which also makes one ask, what can the octopus possibly make of us?

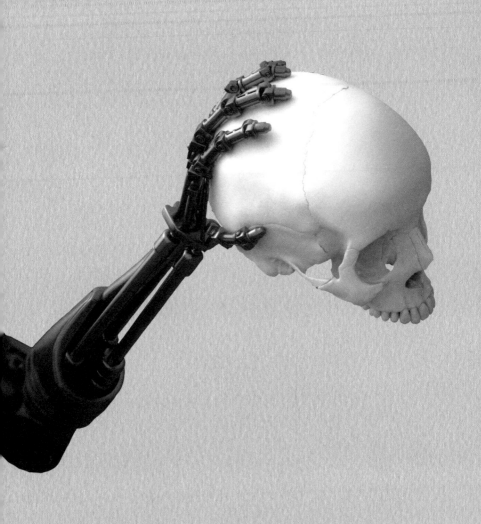

CHAPTER 12

FUTURE BRAINS, FUTURE NEUROSCIENCE

BUILDING NEW BRAINS

Neuroscience is a young discipline. Until the 1960s, researchers were content to be physiologists, psychologists, anatomists, or maybe brain scientists. When the US Society for Neuroscience was founded in 1969 it had members in the hundreds. Its annual meetings now pull up to 40,000 people.

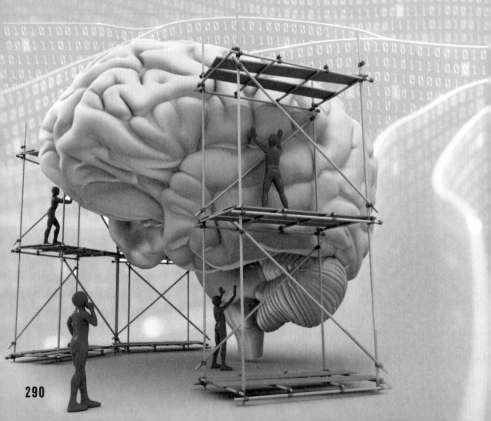

Which is to say, you ain't seen nothing yet. I have tried to take in some history here, but the great mass of neuroscience findings are still new. And the most impressive achievements in understanding the brain probably lie in the future.

Where will they lead? There are bold predictions, and wildly varying opinions about whether they will materialize, and how soon. Something about the importance of the human brain makes it irresistible to speculate. Might we be able to fix it? Make it last longer? Enhance it? Build one like it?

One far-reaching idea is that computers will exceed our brains' capabilities. The boldest scenario envisages uniting with our technology by uploading our minds, existing virtually in a strange new world.

I'm going to stick my neck out and say that this isn't going to happen anytime soon – think centuries, not decades. However, it does seem reasonable to foresee stronger interaction between computer science and technology, and neuroscience.

This is already two-way traffic here, with some interesting loops. There are efforts to simulate organic brains inside supercomputers – the billion euro Human Brain Project in the European Union started out with that goal, though it has proved controversial, with sharp arguments among different neuroscience factions about what such a simulation could tell us, and has changed direction a few times since.

The simulation would rely on software running on digital computers as they are built now. On the other side are projects that try to design computers that follow principles more like those that seem to operate in organic brains. That means parallel processing, breaking down the separation between memory and processing, and other, more radical moves. Perhaps one day the two strands will come together, at least to allow brains and computers to talk to each other more directly than they do now.

THE MIND OF A WORM

Brain research nowadays has billion-dollar budgets with ambitions to match. It can be hard to assess them. Even if we managed to map the entire human connectome, for example (see Chapter 1), what would it tell us?

◀ Sydney Brenner contemplates the worm.

A past research landmark gives a clue. Back in 1963, Sydney Brenner chose the tiny nematode worm *Caenorhabditis elegans* as a model organism that could bridge the gap between molecular biology, then flourishing after the discovery of the DNA structure a decade earlier, and neurobiology. His plan was to produce a complete map of the worm – genes, cells, and all.

It worked. We now have the entire genome, and a developmental map of every cell. It does not exactly have a brain, but the worm certainly has a nervous system. The most common, hermaphroditic, form of the beast has a mere 959 cells, of which 302 are neurons.

Heroic work with electron microscopy, hand tracing of cellular connections, and self-programmed computers produced a complete map of this system, and its 8,000 synapses, in 1984. The complete reference version took up 340 pages of a special edition of the *Philosophical Transactions of the Royal Society*.

And then? Well, there was little immediate insight into how the whole ensemble worked. Rather, knowing the connections allowed researchers to plot better experiments investigating the worm's responses to the world. The connectome – as we would now call it – generated lots of hypotheses, but they had to be tested painstakingly by altering the system, by gene tweaks or by removing cells, and monitoring the effects.

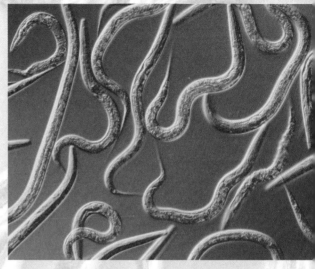

▲ *The nematode gets by with a few hundred neurons, but predicting their action is still challenging.*

Three decades, and many research careers later, we understand much more about how this simple creature senses its surroundings and behaves, but the work still goes on. And an expanded connectome for the male form of the worm, which has an extra 81 neurons, did not appear until 2012. Even in that small collection, there are over 100 different *kinds* of neurons.

All in all, the worm work demonstrates that a wiring diagram is an amazing thing to have, but it is a starting point, not an end point. The same will apply, if we get there, to the connectomes of more complicated organisms like vertebrates, with their more complex neurons.

DATA EXPLOSION

> *"Expecting big data approaches to succeed just because they have lots of data is like expecting to understand how Microsoft Word works by taking the back off your laptop and staring at the wiring."*

Consideration of the human brain quickly leads to big numbers – billions of neurons, trillions of synapses. Neuroscience is generating even bigger numbers now. It is accumulating data at a rate you might call explosive – except explosions are short and sharp, whereas this one just goes on.

It applies to imaging techniques, as mentioned at the beginning of this book, and they'll continue to pile up the terabytes. But future growth will also involve data that researchers hope will improve understanding of how networks of neurons function. Optogenetics that can turn neurons on and off, and new recording techniques that can register changes in activity of hundreds or even thousands of neurons at a time in experimental animals, will drive this.

But that could lead to an ultra-empiricist's nightmare: the problem of understanding how the things the brain can do can emerge from networks of neurons simply gets transformed into another problem – working out what a vast quantity of data about neural networks actually means. As Anne Churchland of the Cold Spring Harbor Laboratory in New York put it in 2016, "it is not clear how to

◀ Anne Churchland.

294

▶ *Neuron action has to tie in with the behaviour of whole creatures – some much more complex than others.*

reduce large and complex data sets into forms that are understandable".

She emphasizes that this will depend on theories to guide the search for patterns in the data. Just mapping connections is little help. A recent study that tried to infer the information processing of a vintage computer chip from a complete simulation of its circuitry showed this rather starkly. Two mischievous researchers applied a series of neuroscience style analyses to the chip. They failed – unsurprisingly according to one commentator, Steve Fleming of University College London, because after all, "expecting big data approaches to succeed just because they have lots of data is like expecting to understand how Microsoft Word works by taking the back off your laptop and staring at the wiring."

NEURON MAPPING

The theories may come from a whole mix of disciplines, including biophysics and computer science, as well as examples of neural circuits that are already relatively well understood. But they will need to be developed alongside studies of the creature that hosts whichever brain yielded the data.

The brain, after all, is there to regulate behaviour. It generates actions that improve the whole organism's prospects in some way. Usually, this relates to the unforgiving calculus of natural selection. In humans it has many, much fuzzier, benefits that may accrue in the course of our social interaction.

Either way, the key theoretical consideration is probably the size of the gap in our understanding between neurons and (most) behaviour. At the moment, researchers can connect neural networks with only the simplest actions of simple creatures. Watch what happens when a fruit fly maggot feels a puff of air, for example. It can either pull its head back, or turn it to the side. How does it choose? Neuron mapping and optogenetics to turn cells on and off can now answer that at the cellular level.

With anything more complex, the going is much harder. As a critique of data-driven approaches made by John Krakauer of Johns Hopkins University and colleagues in 2017 put it, we do not usually know what the relevant level of brain organization is for any given behaviour.

Like the fruit fly watchers, Krakauer and co are focusing on non-human brains, and on behaviour that can be studied systematically. That might be as simple as the movement of a nematode worm in its dish. But what about a rodent dashing for cover when it senses a diving hawk, a bat catching insects on the fly in a forest at night, or a troupe of macaques grooming each other? It is crucial to design experiments that help get a fix on what level is most important for the behaviour of interest. Misunderstand that, and you are on the wrong side of an argument made in the 1980s by neurophysiologist David Marr, who urged that "trying to understand perception by understanding neurons is like trying to understand a bird's flight by studying only feathers."

Underlying the discussion is the question: what does it actually mean to understand an operation of the brain, anyway?

I've fudged that often in this book by saying things like a part of the brain "is involved" in this or that function. Everyone does it. But describing neural circuits, in ever-increasing detail, doesn't necessarily increase understanding. Criticizing those who seem to suggest it is a contemporary refraction of the debate about how far to pursue reductionism (see Chapter 2). You won't understand the brain one neuron at a time, says Krakauer, any more than you will comprehend the patterns made by a flock of starlings by studying one, or even a few, birds. Things emerge from the collective in both cases.

You can see all this as a fundamental difference in approach between brain mappers and students of behaviour. But perhaps it is more a matter of emphasis. After all, Krakauer and his colleagues still believe that behaviour is a product of brains that use algorithms of some sort, and computational processing, all carried out by ensembles of neurons.

◀ The murmuration of a giant flock of starlings emerges from thousands of individual movements.

CAN ANYONE PLAY?

Data banks are overflowing with brain images and neural mapping coordinates. Computers will help make sense of them. But for some kinds of analysis human brains are still the best processors available. The problem is recruiting enough of them.

One way is to open up research to citizen scientists. Online access to data has allowed laypeople to contribute to several fields where there is a surplus of data over eyeballs, including galactic astronomy and the biochemistry of protein folding.

Neuroscience is getting in on the act. Eyewire, an online game launched in 2010, gets players to work on electron micrographs of the retina. Each round of play traces branches of a neuron across a cube 4.5μm (micrometers) wide, in collaboration with an algorithm. The human players resolve ambiguities that bamboozle the computer, and can compete to reach new levels in the game. Hundreds of thousands of players helped build up the first three-dimensional (3D) map of the mouse retina. In 2017, a revised game was opened that maps neurons in the zebrafish.

Mozak (the word for brain in Serbo-Croat) from the University of Washington is a browser-based game that involves players in classifying neurons according to the shapes of their cell bodies, axonal

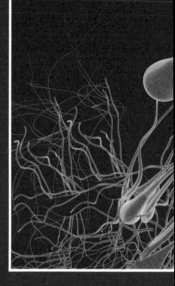

▼ *Brain-mapper Sebastian Seung of MIT helped devise Eyewire.*

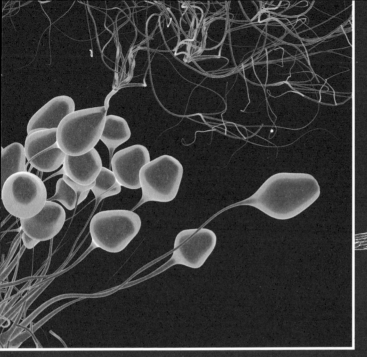

◄ *Close-up of neuronal columns in a zebrafish brain.*

links and dendritic trees. All of these vary enormously, and there is an as yet uncharted variety in the overall form an individual neuron and its connections can adopt. A well-researched catalogue of these forms will help reveal which kinds of cells do what in the brain, and how they may go awry. Players help build the catalogue by tracing connections from individual neurons in 3D. This takes practice, and new contributors gradually gain experience in tracing, reviewing and editing reconstructions of single neurons. Each cell is traced by at least five people to minimize errors. Professionals, of course, can play the game too, and some have found that they work faster using the interface the game-coders have built. But there is ample scope for more players. With 86 billion neurons in the human brain, there are plenty to go round.

CONTROLLING NEURONS

While the brain builders raise their game, there is work to do improving manipulation of already existing brains. The overarching goal is to take control of individual neurons (setting aside the small problem of working out what an individual neuron does).

Micro-electrodes can do that nowadays but require drilling into the skull. Optogenetic tricks (see Chapter 2) offer some improvement, but light does not penetrate far without a fibre-optic tube, which still requires penetrating the head.

One alternative approach to engineering cells for control is to substitute receptors that respond to custom-made chemicals rather than light signals. For neurons, the idea is to tailor neurotransmitter receptors to respond to a new messenger. Such a receptor has been creatively named DREADD, for Designer Receptor Exclusively Activated by Designer Drugs.

There is a model system, using acetylcholine receptors that have been mutated so that they are activated by a non-biological compound known as clozapine-N-oxide. In animal experiments this has been used to activate or deactivate target neurons, depending on the specific receptor used.

◀ *Gold nanoparticles can be absorbed by cells, including neurons.*

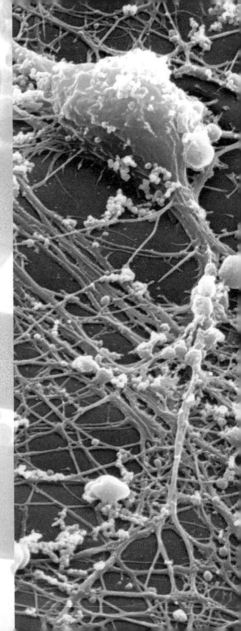

▶ *Neurons growing in culture.*

This has the same drawback as optogenetics, in that it involves use of a genetically engineered virus to alter cells, and an extra one: the designer drug is a free-floating molecule so cannot be targeted as accurately as a light signal.

NANOPARTICLES

Another alternative could avoid both those problems. Metal nanoparticles can be introduced into cells and heated up by electromagnetic fields or even ultrasound. If such particles sit inside a neuron, and are heated just right, it may fire. It's been called "optogenetics without the genetics".

This is not a tried-and-tested idea yet. But examples of work with gold nanoparticles, in particular, are mounting up. Tiny metal spheres or rods are given an inert coating to minimize unwanted effects, and can be taken up by cells. They heat up when exposed to a pulse from a laser.

There are reports of such treatment helping to activate nerve growth after spinal cord injuries, activating neuronal ion channels, and promoting or inhibiting firing of neurons in culture. Expect to hear more about this kind of treatment of brain cells as experimenters grow more confident in handling nanomaterials.

BRAIN TRAINING

A comfortably non-intrusive way of acting on the brain has had a lot of publicity in recent years. The "use it or lose it" principle has been applied to the brain, inspired by studies of neural plasticity and potentiation of synapses. And some have built on the idea by designing "brain-training" games.

They have prompted controversy, partly because commercial offerings may come with exaggerated claims. An open letter from 70 neuroscientists in 2014 charged that "consumers are told that playing brain games will make them smarter, more alert, and able to learn faster and better", but that data to back this up is hard to come by. They were particularly critical of suggestions that games can slow age-related decline in cognitive skills.

The letter drew a response from a slightly larger group, with similar credentials, critiquing the critique.

Both groups agreed that such claims call for controlled studies, that they are hard to do, and that it is harder still to show benefits outside the domain of the game. That is, training your brain may improve performance, but perhaps only on the task you have worked on – which, being artificial, probably isn't much use to you. Incidentally, the same applies to exposure to music, supposedly an intelligence booster via the so-called "Mozart effect". It may help you appreciate Mozart, but that's all.

However, there are tantalizing findings about the effects of certain video games. For example, an admittedly rather small study from the University

◀ Use it or lose it.

of California in 2013 found that a driving game, Neuroracer, involving multitasking (guiding a virtual car while reading signs) enhanced older subjects' game performance to the level of (untrained) 20-year-olds, and had wider benefits on attention and working memory.

A later study suggests that a pattern-recognition app called Game Show can benefit people with "amnestic mild cognitive impairment" – regarded as an early indicator of dementia. Playing the game for two hours a week showed improvements in episodic memory compared with a control group with the same symptoms.

Again, the study needs larger-scale follow up. But it reinforces the impression that the immediate prospect might be for slowing cognitive decline rather than brain boosts for everyone.

▼ A still from Neuroracer, which has been used in studies of how to improve multi-tasking.

TECHNO-BRAINS

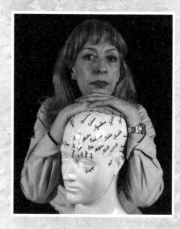

▼ Susan Greenfield is worried.

We marvel at new technologies, but are ambivalent about their effects. With computers and information technology, this often takes the form of worrying about what they might do to our brains.

This anxiety taps into old fears about the modern world moving too fast for us to cope with. But there are more specific concerns about the internet and computer games in particular.

The Oxford University neuroscientist Susan Greenfield, for example, has argued that our brains adapt to the environment and that, as it is now changing in unprecedented ways, we should be open to the possibility of unprecedented effects.

Her 2015 book *Mind Change* suggests they could include social networking eroding communication skills and undermining empathy, gaming producing reckless players with shortened attention spans, and search engines inducing a preference for superficial surfing rather than gaining deep understanding.

Her knowledge of some of these domains, especially gaming, seems limited, but her list does point to researchable questions. Mostly, the research has yet to be done.

Meantime, a more reassuring view is that, yes, the internet and other technologies are changing our brains. They respond to experience, just as they have always done. Specifying what those changes are, good or bad, is not possible at the moment. The most likely outcome is that they will enhance some capacities of our adaptable brains, and diminish others. For example, internet access means no longer having to remember information. Instead, we prioritize remembering where to find it. In return, we get access to vastly more of it than ever before.

Another long view of our brains' relationship with technology is also more positive. Philosopher Andy Clark sees technology, which our brains allow us to create, as a way to increase their reach. The augmented brain or, as he puts it, extended mind exists because our brains have evolved to allow a kind of technological bootstrapping. From writing and the abacus to clocks, maps, the pocket calculator and the internet-enabled smartphone, we delegate tasks that once would have relied on our brains to convenient devices. Lazy? No, think of it as progressively outsourcing cognitive enhancement.

▼ *The pilot flying a modern aircraft outsources a lot of information processing.*

PLUGGING IN

If uploading your mind into a giant computer is not in prospect, what about the opposite manoeuvre, linking up with a machine to get information into your head?

Since William Gibson, the speculative fiction author who coined the term cyberspace, depicted people of the future "jacking in" in his 1984 novel *Neuromancer*, the idea of bypassing human–machine interfaces by making a direct connection with a computer has fired some people's hopes. The latest is the high-tech entrepreneur Elon Musk, who in 2017 launched a new venture, Neuralink, aiming to make a "neural lace" that might mesh with the brain and interact with individual synapses.

The company's initial focus is on helping people with brain injuries, building on devices like the cochlear implant – which restores hearing via the nerves in the ear – and experimental devices that can offer glimmers of vision to people with retinal disease.

◀ *William Gibson, inventor of cyberspace.*

▶ *Elon Musk, inventor of neural lace.*

Neural lace would have to be integrated with deeper brain tissue, though, and make many more connections than these. At the moment, experiments with neurons connected to computer chips, or computer circuits that use neurons grown from stem cells, are very small scale and strictly for the lab bench. No one knows how such entities would fare inside real brains, but living tissue often reacts adversely to artificial implants.

The company has not said what technology it thinks will help make something small enough to interface with the brain from the inside. Nor is it clear how it might get round the fact that we know little about how information is coded in a way that the brain can use.

It is likely that any advances toward Musk's vision will come first on the side of taking signals generated by the brain to devices outside – rather than the other way round. The US Defense Advanced Research Projects Agency has projects that could contribute to that, too.

Musk, though, has a higher-level goal than better control of weapon systems.

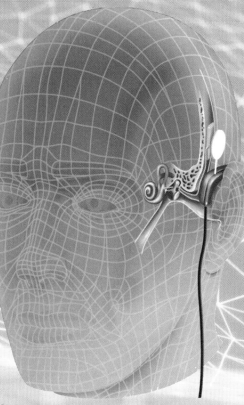

▲ Cochlear implants can restore sensitivity to sound to many deaf subjects.

He believes that neural lace will one day be essential for us to communicate effectively with artificial intelligences yet to be built that will vastly surpass human abilities. Perhaps by the time we have one, we will also have the other.

EXTENDED SENSES

Brain–computer interfaces remain largely speculative. But a more basic approach already shows promise of extending our senses.

David Eagleman of Stanford University argues that the brain has a generalized ability to process information, which our senses plug into. And we can adapt to new inputs, as when someone who has gone blind learns to read Braille by touch.

Transforming other input signals into patterns of touch can extend our senses into new realms, Eagleman suggests. All sensation, in the end, is electrochemical activity in the brain, and it doesn't matter how it is stimulated.

His lab has experimented with a wearable vest (a Versatile Extra-Sensory Transducer) rigged up with a few dozen tiny motors that vibrate. If these are linked to a system that converts sounds into patterns of vibrations felt on the back and chest, deaf people can learn to decode spoken language. Unlike Braille text, the sound is not coded, just broken down into different frequencies.

But why stop at sensory substitution? Eagleman and his colleagues want to experiment by linking the vest array to other data streams. He believes it could be used to generate entirely new senses. Other creatures can see in the infrared, or hear ultrasonic frequencies. Why not us?

▲ *David Eagleman demonstrates the wearable vest – Versatile Extra-Sensory Transducer.*

And there are speculative applications for people who want to control complex systems. That could be someone in a virtual reality game who gets information about the game environment by touch. One experiment linked the vest to a data stream from a remote-controlled helicopter drone, so the pilot could feel its movements and respond more rapidly than is possible for someone just watching the machine from ground level. One day, says Eagleman, an astronaut might "feel" the state of the International Space Station instead of monitoring consoles and read-outs. Or perhaps a politician giving a speech would be able to sense global reaction by being linked to a real-time assessment of tweets, relayed to the vest.

A crowd-funded company is working on a more widely available version of the vest, which involves some delicate engineering. But the general principle sounds powerful. Treat the brain as a generally capable computational device, then decide what new inputs you would like to try.

▼ A neural vest could be handy worn underneath a space suit.

SO, WHAT IS A BRAIN *MOST* LIKE?

What is it like to be someone else (or a bat), is the question philosophers like to pose. But the history of efforts to answer, "What is the brain like?" is fascinating too.

Here's what we do with our human brains, and all their experience. Show us something we don't quite grasp, and we try to think what it might resemble. The answer for brains, usually, has been the most impressively complicated and clever thing we knew at the time.

Descartes, struck by water-powered automata built for the French king in the 17th century, proposed the brain and nerves might be basically hydraulic. By the 19th century, somewhat unexpectedly, you can find people comparing the brain to a piano – playing a melody captured in "cortical vibrations". Alternatively, individual cells were piano keys, a small number of components that play an infinity of music.

Later, brains resembled railway switching systems, early factory automation efforts, and – as you can still see in dog-eared children's books – the telephone exchange, not to mention Sherrington's "enchanted loom" weaving its ever shifting neural patterns.

In fact, most complex human creations have been invoked when someone tries to fathom the brain. Cities, and parts of cities, are especially popular. Photography influences thinking about memory, and holograms had their day too. Phonograph records and telegraph signals crop up. Neuron functions are likened to electronic valves.

More recently, computers furnish many comparisons for brain functions. We now know lots of ways brains differ from our standard model, one-instruction-at-a-time digital computers. That doesn't matter too much. Metaphors and analogies are there to help generate ideas to test out. Besides, the computer analogy is unlikely to fade until there is something else to take its place. What that might be is for future neuroscientists to ponder.

Meanwhile, I have an intriguing paper on my desk on which parts of the brain are active when metaphors in different domains are invoked. "Kicking a habit", for example, seems to prompt thoughts of actual kicking, or at least involve motor areas of the cortex. Perhaps one day we shall take scanning round the next loop, and study how the brain processes metaphors about itself.

INDEX

Entries in *italic* indicate books unless otherwise stated.

PICTURE CREDITS

Every effort has been made to trace copyright holders and to obtain their permission for the use of copyright material. The publisher apologizes for any errors or omissions and would be grateful if notified of any corrections that should be incorporated in future reprints or editions of this book.

(tr), 236 (b), 238 (b), 239 (b), 240–1, 242 (t), 243 (t), 244, 245, 246 (c & b), 247, 253 (tr & bl), 255 (t & b), 257, 260, 262, 264 (b), 268, 269 (t & b), 272 (tr), 274 (b), 278 (b), 279 (t), 282 (t), 288, 290 (b), 291 (b), 292, 293, 298–9 (t), 300, 301, 304 (t), 307 (r).

Alamy
• •

10 (tr), 11 (br), 12 (bl), 13 (br), 15 (bl & br), 16, 17 (br), 18 (t & b), 19 (b), 21 (t & b), 57, 59, 273 (tr), 306 (br).

Getty
• •

10 (b), 22, 23 (tl), 24 (bl), 29 (t & b), 38 (c), 46, 73, 78 (br), 130, 169, 170, 187 (b), 189 (c), 193, 207 (t), 208 (tr), 223 (t), 229, 236 (t), 251, 265, 270, 280 (t), 284 (bl & br), 294, 298 (b), 304 (b), 306 (bc), 308 (cr).

iStock
• •

8, 15 (bc), 28, 75, 79 (br), 80 (bl & br), 121, 129, 144, 159 (t), 216, 242–3 (b), 252, 261.

Shutterstock
• •

6–7, 11 (bl), 12 (r), 14 (l & r), 18–19, 31 (l), 33 (t & b), 36, 38 (t & b), 39, 40–1, 43, 44 (l), 45 (r), 47, 48, 49, 50–1 (t & b)), 52, 53 (b), 54–5, 55 (t), 62–3 (b), 64–5, 66, 68 (br), 69, 70–1, 72 (t), 72–3, 74, 76–7, 78–9 (b & t), 80 (c), 81, 85 (tr), 86, 87 (b), 88 (t & b), 89, 90–1, 90 (c), 91 (c), 92, 93, 94 (t & b), 95, 96 (t & b), 97 (b & r), 100–1, 103 (br), 104 (tr), 104–5, 106, 107, 115 (b), 118, 120–1, 124 (tl & tr), 126 (t), 127, 128, 131, 132–3, 134 (b), 134–5, 135 (r), 136–7, 137 (b), 141 (bl), 142, 148 (tr & bl), 149, 150–1 (t & b), 151 (c), 152–3, 153 (b), 154, 156–7, 159 (c), 160, 162–3, 163 (t), 164 (t), 164–5, 165 (c), 166–7, 168, 171, 173, 174–5, 175 (b), 176–7, 178–9, 180, 182, 183, 184–5, 186 (t & c), 188, 194 (tr & br), 197 (r), 198 (t), 198–9, 199 (b), 200, 201, 202–3, 203 (t), 207 (b), 210–11, 210 (b), 212 tl & bl), 213 (r), 214 (tr), 214–15, 217, 220, 222 (b), 222–3, 226–7, 227 (b), 228, 230–1, 231 (bl & tr)), 232–3, 234 (cr & bl), 234–5, 237, 238–9, 240 (t), 241 (b), 248, 248–9, 252–3, 254, 256, 258 (bl), 263, 264 (tl), 266, 267, 272–3, 274 (t), 275, 276, 277, 278–9, 280–1, 282 (b), 283, 285, 286–7 (b), 287 (t), 290–1, 295 (t & c), 296–7, 298–9, 302, 303 (tl), 305, 306–7, 308–9, 309 (b), 310 (t, c, & b), 311 (l & r), all other background effects not directly listed.